EPICURUS MY MASTER

EPICURUS MY MASTER

BY

MAX RADIN

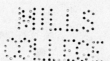
Chapel Hill
THE UNIVERSITY
of North Carolina
PRESS

COPYRIGHT 1949 BY

THE UNIVERSITY OF NORTH CAROLINA PRESS

MANUFACTURED IN THE UNITED STATES OF AMERICA

VAN REES PRESS, NEW YORK

PJ

TO DOROTHEA

to whom Atticus was an old friend

INTRODUCTION

By Huntington Cairns

Atticus kept no diary, he wrote no autobiography, and his letters to Cicero are lost. Professor Radin, however, has had the happy thought of presenting Atticus to us as he imagines Atticus might have portrayed himself had he written his reminiscences. Professor Radin's sympathy with the Epicureanism of Atticus—humanistic in its ethical outlook, scientific in its view of the world—is assurance that the intellectual scheme he outlines is one that Atticus himself would have wished communicated.

Atticus belongs to that minority of men who, through discipline and art, have made themselves what they desire to be. He is in the ranks of those who contrive to lead the kind of lives they contemplate. Most men live according to chance, with no intent save that measured by expediency. If the test of happiness is to have no cause for regrets, then Atticus ranks among the happiest of men.

He is also one of the tantalizing figures of history. No one, I venture to think, has read Cicero's letters to him without wanting to know more; little they tell us accounts for the attitude of his contemporaries towards him. His life was spent

vii

during one of the most unsettled periods of history, the time of the Roman Civil Wars, the fall of the Republic, the establishment of the Monarchy. With the dark politics of those murderous days Atticus resolved to have nothing to do. He renounced all public honors although they were easily within the grasp of a man of his wealth and position. He believed, we are told by his friend and biographer, Cornelius Nepos, that men who sail in the troubled waters of politics have no more freedom of direction than they who are tossed on the waves of the ocean. To the men of his time who put their lives, families, and fortunes in jeopardy for their beliefs, such a reason ought to have seemed specious, if not cowardly. Politicians like Bolingbroke have thought his conduct infamous in this respect.

Yet in Atticus' youth he was admired and sought out by Sulla; in his old age he was courted by Augustus. He was the friend of Cicero as well as of Hortensius, of Brutus as well as of Antony, of Marius as well as of Sulla; the Athenians put up statues to him, the Romans respected and revered him. Nor is this all: He survived the Civil Wars, the invasions and the proscriptions of the first century B.C., not through insignificance, inaction or poverty, but in spite of his prominence, his dangerous friendships, and his wealth. He did not hesitate to give assistance to the declared public enemies of the state, such as Marius the younger, Mark Antony, and Brutus, when the fortunes of those warriors were at their ebb. This course of conduct did not seem to Atticus' friends to be of such calculated prudence that there could be no respect for it. Whatever may be the verdict of the remote observers of later days, to Roman contemporaries of all parties the friendship of Atticus was one of their most valued possessions.

The conflict that faces the man who would be both prudent and just was of great interest to Cicero, who, at least in his extant writings, never resolved it. Atticus' life exemplifies this conflict. But even his most skilful defender, Lady Mary Wortley Montagu, sees more prudence than justice in his career. He was the only Roman, she believed, who had a true notion of the times in which he lived. The Republic was doomed, and the two factions which pretended to support it were equally endeavoring to gratify their ambition in its ruin; in a storm, when all is lost, it is proper for the best hands to try to reach the shore. Professor Radin attempts a different and sounder solution of the ethical problem of Atticus' life, as set against the background of one of the decisive centuries of the Western World. We have in the present volume an account, by an American classical scholar, of events and ideas during the latter part of the first century B.C. as Atticus might have written it. The philosophy expressed here is that which is concerned with man's present, not his possible future, happiness. In all this the perceptive reader will not overlook the suggestion for our own period at which Professor Radin hints.

PREFACE

The purpose of this book is to record an escape. It is an escape well enough authenticated, but it occurred under unique circumstances against an historical background which is perhaps the most stirring and exciting in recorded history, the background of the century-long Roman revolution that determined the form and character of Western civilization.

That Atticus, living at that time, under circumstances of this sort, was able to effect an escape from a crashing world and still cull from it all that it had of grace and fragrance, was due to circumstances not likely to be repeated. He was rich and he had steeped himself in a philosophy that provided in complete detail for just the way of living that he chose. But except for his temperament and strength of mind, he would not have chosen it and could not have accomplished his purpose.

I have sought to depict the society in which he moved and in which he was a striking and unique figure. All of the important persons here mentioned, all of the important events, are matters of history. If in setting them forth, I have varied from the standard accounts, it is done deliberately, generally because I find myself unable to accept the standard interpretation of many of the facts, neither the exaltation of these personages, which we owe to the Renaissance, nor the denigration, which was chiefly the work of nineteenth-century Germany.

The minor characters and events, most of which are invented, are, I feel confident, in complete accordance with probabilities as I have derived them from long and loving engrossment in the study of the period.

I think Atticus, who lived beyond the ordinary span of years in accordance with principles that permitted the fullest use of life, was for all his mastery of the art of living, an unhappy man. He loved his friends, but he did not love his fellow men. The one thing lacking was to come from an element in our present civilization that sprang neither from Athens nor from Rome, but from the Judaean hills and the Brook of Kedron.

M. R.

EPICURUS MY MASTER

"MY FRIEND ATTICUS." That is how the old satyr, Lucius Sulla,* presented me to his guests fifty years ago—more than fifty years ago. And that is how our young imperator, I am told, refers to me in his letters and conversation. Only Sulla said, "My young friend, Atticus." And Caesar, I suppose, says, or means to be understood as saying, "My venerable friend." That is one of the penalties of living to be seventy-seven. I am sorry for it. I never particularly wanted to be venerated.

There is another penalty in living so long. I have survived all the men I grew up with, and have seen them die—tragically enough, most of them, alas! Indeed, a little of me must have died with each one of them. Young Marius was the first, and if I live another year or so it looks as though Marcus and Quintus will not have been the last. A long procession. If my end should come tonight, I could not complain of being too suddenly confronted with dissolution; I have had plenty of practice in dying.

And if I have survived so many persons, I have also survived something a little more important. I have survived my country. The extraordinary young protégé of Maecenas, who writes

* See Dramatis Personae, pp. 137-42.

I

hexameters as even my dear Lucretius could not, put it in a single phrase in the lines he read to us last week: *superavimus urbi*. What new country will arise on the site of the Rome now dead I cannot tell. Events are hurrying on. Whether it will be my friend Marcus Antonius or my friend Caesar Octavian who will build the new state is of little moment. It will not be my sort of state, nor shall I live to see it.

To be sure, as things look now, I shall not have to live very long to witness the decision. The reports I have been receiving from the East—my informants have been accurate for a half century, so that I have abundant reason to trust them—the reports I have been receiving make it quite certain that Antonius will move westward to Thrace this next month and that Caesar will have to take up the challenge. There is a way out, at any rate for the present, but it can hardly be more than a truce. And it means the sacrifice of an admirable woman. Poor Octavia! A sweet and gentle creature. A thousand pities that she should be the pawn in such a struggle.

Saras writes that the Egyptian has no intention of letting Antonius fight if she can prevent it. I fancy she will not have the last word. After all, my son-in-law will count for something here.

And since I speak of my son-in-law, I ought to qualify what I have said before. I have survived those friends I knew as a boy and as a young man. Marius, Hortensius, Torquatus, the two Ciceros, Gaius Caesar—he is a god now, and I trust he has learned what he never possessed in life, the beatitude of indifference—Gnaeus Pompeius, Appius Claudius, Marcus Cato, Manius Lepidus, Aulus Hirtius—they all are gone, these friends of mine. But without arrogance I may say I never lacked the power of making new ones. For one thing, my good Nepos is, I am sure, my friend. Then there is that clever Spaniard, Balbus.

2

I think he is really attached to me, as he was to Caesar and Cicero. And Agrippa, to whom I gave my beloved child, was my friend before he became my son-in-law. I have a notion that the young stepson of Caesar—they have betrothed my baby granddaughter to him: honor enough for a mere Roman knight!—he, too, has become fond of me. A rather solemn boy, this nine-year-old Tiberius Nero, something new in the Claudian stock.

Well, Agrippa and Balbus are both out of Rome for a week or so, and in their absence there is no one to incite that silly Greek doctor to persecute me with his drugs and simples. I think, therefore, I shall give myself a respite for a while from the wretched pain that has so suddenly and unexpectedly begun to torture a peaceable Epicurean; one, moreover, who has scorned to consult a physician for a generation of mortal men. They tell me that if I don't eat regularly I shall die. That may be so. And if I do eat I am in agony for hours. This nonsense has got to end. When they come back, Agrippa and Balbus, I shall have it out with them. I can always deceive my darling Atticula about my condition. I am not sure I should have been so successful had her mother lived. Poor thing, she knew what illness was.

To be seventy-seven and to suffer excruciating pain in the bowels—those are two drastic reminders of mortality, the one of soul and the other of body. And when the atoms composing my soul—those of my body I suspect are good for little except some cosmic scrap heap—when my soul's atoms perform their famous swerve, I wonder what will happen to them. Certainly I could wish them a worse fate than to be recombined into the person of a man, even if the days he falls on are as troubled and bitter and bloody as those of my time.

Bitter and bloody and troubled they have been. I was a boy

3

when old Marius rolled up along the Sacred Street in the Cimbrian triumph, but although I felt a personal connection with it, I remember with even greater clearness the street fights when Glaucia and Saturninus were taken and killed. That happened almost within the same year. And ever since that time up to the day when I am writing this, the one question in the mind of Romans is whether this or that man will be their master. At least, it will be a Roman master. That is something to be thankful for. Unless, indeed, Antonius foists the Egyptian's bastard on us. Who his father was I should hesitate to say. I am fairly certain I know who his father was not.

Strange that so many of them, these bloody and bitter men, should have been my friends even while they hated each other. I think they really were my friends. I have not escaped a little suspicion on that account. More than a little suspicion. Pollio said it courteously and Veratius said it spitefully: "There are two classes of men with whom one does not quarrel, prospective testators and indulgent creditors."

Would they have been my friends if I had been poor? Perhaps not. My life would have been different, of course, if my father had not left me a fortune and my uncle a still larger one, if I had no estates at Buthrotum, no house on the Quirinal, no establishment at Athens. But it was certainly not merely my wealth. After all, Crassus and Lentulus and Lucullus were far richer, and Marcus Cato almost as rich. These men had their friends, but I should say more men hated them than loved them. Few have hated me and many have loved me. If I were to write my epitaph, I might select that.

Evidently, men like me will soon be forgotten. My good Marcus Cicero was quite sure he would be famous forever. I am certain he will be. Gaius Catullus was right. No Roman ever wrote or spoke, or ever will, as beautifully as Marcus

4

Tullius did. Much good it will do the swerving atoms that once made up Marcus' soul!

I have no special desire to be remembered. I could scarcely be an Epicurean and desire it. And I must claim this much justice: I have made no strenuous effort to secure it. I might have bequeathed to my Atticula a waxen image with the titles and dates of my offices: *Quintus Caecilius Q. f. Pomponianus Atticus, consul, praetor, tr. pl., quaestor*—perhaps, *imperator, legatus, tr. mil.* That was attainable. Indeed, I had to make a distinct effort to avoid it. Or I might have written a few books, somewhat more substantial than the four or five scrolls I have amused myself with. I am not sure that my literary capacity is less than Varro's. Or else I might have built in Athens, or in Rome, structures that would perpetuate my name, a *porticus Pomponiana* or a *theatrum Caecilianum*. It would have been a foolish waste of money, and much that was better than money, my time and my peace of mind.

I am not so simple as to believe that I ever attained peace of mind. Only the gods have *ataraxy,* and to their blissful company I do not aspire. Gaius Caesar, it seems, is of them now. It is an interesting speculation to wonder how they get on, Caesar and the gods; Caesar was so very much of a man. In Homer's Olympus he would have been quite at home. I fear he will be bored in the intermundial spaces which, we are taught by our Master Epicurus, is the real abode of the gods.

No, I cannot assert that I ever attained *ataraxy,* or anything really like it. Much has disturbed me in my long life, much that a more fully initiated spirit might have borne without quivering. It broke my heart when I took leave of my boyhood companion, Marius, the brilliant young soldier who was to pay the penalty of being the son of the conqueror of the Cimbri. I never saw him again. I am not ashamed of the tears I wept

5

then. After all, I was twenty-four. Rome lost much when he died. Whether he could have been used to advantage is more doubtful. He was terribly on the wrong side.

Then there were the dreadful days when I sought refuge in the house of Volumnius during the Terror. I can honestly say I was not afraid for my own life. But there were Pillia and Atticula. And quite apart from imminent danger to them or to me I discovered that even a life spent, as mine had been, in constant contemplation of cruelty and rapine had not been sufficiently hardened. It shook the pride in my humanity to see men hunt each other like wild beasts, sometimes without even the poor justification of vengeance or avarice.

That was a dreadful period. Whatever happens, I do not believe it will occur again, whether Antonius wins or Caesar. Occasionally, none the less, I wonder. There is a kind of relentless singleness of purpose in Octavian which will always discover a new reason for what he wishes done. And Antonius, drunk or sober, can be guilty of such extravagant enormities that I can readily see why the Dictator failed to choose him as his successor. Still, it is too recent, the Terror of ten years ago. After all, forty years elapsed between the Terror of Sulla and that of the Commission of Three. It must be remembered that I lived through both of them.

How can I explain that I survived when so many men perished? We Epicureans do not deal with fate or with fortune. There are no favorites of the gods. I rallied Sulla on his title of *Felix*. He grinned at me and said it was worth six legions to be supposed to deserve it. But he took it seriously, I verily believe, for all that. Not good fortune was mine, nor yet uniformly good judgment, although I dare boast my judgment was as good as Marcus Cicero's and better than Pompeius'. I have made serious blunders. I was wrong enough about Caesar's

6

conduct when he came back from Gaul, and about Marcus Brutus' character.

Certainly I should not think of rating myself on a par with most of the men I have called my friends, in force, in vigor of mind, or in talents. If I succeeded where they failed, it is, I believe, because, like Titus Lucretius, I had the best of guidance. Our Master Epicurus saved us from fear and the shadow of fear. That would have been enough in all conscience. But more than that, he taught us that life was a whole which could be fully grasped in the mind of any enlightened man. Perhaps the difference between me and these others—I was not the only Epicurean in Rome—was that I grasped it and held it. Most of them grasped it and lost it and spent their lives perpetually pursuing it.

I never broke faith with any man or woman. I never exploited man or woman. I took all that life could give me. I have neither sought unnecessary suffering nor avoided necessary pain.

And I have no intention of being bullied in my old age by an Agrigentine quack.

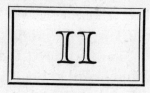

II

I OWE MY UNCLE, Quintus Caecilius, a great deal. And I do not mean wholly or even chiefly the ten millions of sesterces and the establishment on the Quirinal that he left me, or the name that his testamentary adoption imposed on me. My friends in Greece have greatly misunderstood this matter. Adoptions at Rome—especially by will—are not quite the same things as they are in Athens or Ephesus or Alexandria. When the Comitia duly ratified my uncle's will, my name was thereafter carried on the census lists as Quintus Caecilius, but to the world I remained Titus Pomponius. It would have been silly to rename a man of fifty-three for purposes of ordinary social intercourse, and no one dreamed of doing it. So, Marcus Brutus became officially Quintus Caepio on the census lists when his uncle adopted him; but no one thought of turning the bearer of the most famous name in Rome into a man of another name, even though he was scarcely twenty-five and even though the Caepios were of ancient nobility. He was Marcus Brutus when he was born and he remained Marcus Brutus when, after Philippi, he drove his sword into his heart.

My uncle, Quintus Caecilius, whose son I became by process

8

of law, was a strange person. He was rich, he was bad-tempered, he was sullen and unsocial; he was, I cannot deny it, avaricious. And he greatly increased his wealth, as I have increased mine, by being a banker, in which profession many of the qualities he possessed were not especially helpful. Certainly no man was less accommodating, no man seemed less willing to attract others to him, although the majority of moneylenders in Rome actively competed for the patronage of spendthrifts and investors.

What I learned from my uncle Quintus was, first of all, extreme care in business methods. He took enormous pains in his accounts. It was the only thing he loved to do and he did it himself. He would trust no slave to do it. Indeed, except for me, he allowed no man to look at his tablets. He said it was to keep the secrets of those who applied to him. That is nonsense. There was no secret about it. Everyone knew. People could scarcely help knowing. He took ample security and put his slaves and freedmen into possession at the first opportunity. The point was that he was by nature a secretive person and he enjoyed the actual management of his complicated affairs. I never saw wax tablets so carefully written.

I remember when that graceless young spendthrift, Lamia, sat in his anteroom while my uncle was transcribing into his records the two talents he lent him. Lamia rose a dozen times, bit his lips, broke out into exclamations of impatience, said he was in a great hurry and, really, he would trust my uncle's memory for the terms. My uncle imperturbably wrote on in his careful cursive, checked up each item, had Tyndarus, his man of affairs, weigh each piece painstakingly, compare his debit and credit tablets, as he always did, three times—he was superstitious about the number three—and acted as though Lamia were not present. Then the money was handed—not to Lamia;

9

the young fop never carried anything that would disturb the plies of his toga—but to an attending slave, and my uncle, looking up, said drily, "You understand one thing, Lucius Aelius, I never renew."

That was his principle. He never renewed. He lent for whatever period seemed to be needed. He never charged more interest than two and never less than one per cent a month. And on the due date he expected payment. If it was not forthcoming, he began his action the next law day. He never abated a jot of his demands. If he was paid—and generally he was paid, men feared him—he might, after an interval, lend again, but it would be a real interval. He was not easy to hoodwink.

He had plenty of clients. Rome was always full of men who were land poor or property poor. They had abundant means, but they needed cash. They could easily and profitably have sold some part of their property, but this they could not persuade themselves to do. They were just the sort of persons who came to my uncle.

And he grew rich. He left, besides land, about thirteen million sesterces, most of which came to me. One quarter of it went to trusted freedmen and to my sister. My good Nepos declares that I reaped the reward of my piety. Be it so. I did not think of my conduct toward my uncle as a particular exemplification of piety. It never occurred to me to act otherwise. Nor was it difficult. His outbursts of temper were quite without any effect on me. I should as soon have been annoyed at the barking of Erotion, my Atticula's little Maltese dog. And my uncle never asked me to do anything that a man, and a nephew, might not properly do.

He was avaricious, I have said. That is certainly not an attractive quality. And he had a worse one. He was miserly. He hated spending money. His Quirinal estate was little better than a farm villa. There were no gardens. The trees around were very much like an unpruned little wood. There was practically no statuary, no painting, except the usual crude frescoes at the hearth and about the lararium. I have changed all that; within moderation, to be sure.

He was miserly in his daily life. He never gave banquets. He kept the old Roman habit of sitting at table—not reclining. I doubt whether meat was served at his Quirinal house once a month. The usual fare consisted of olives, mallows, and apples or other vegetables in season, washed down by a sharp Falernian. Nothing was more amusing than to watch Lucullus at my uncle's house. Lucullus was very nearly his sole intimate. And when I say amusing, I mean that Lucullus was amused, as well as I. He would go through the form of dilating on the particular taste of a vegetable marrow as though he were praising a new dish at a banquet of Crassus or of his own. My uncle would mutter, "Jeer, jeer away, my good friend. If you dine with me, you'll eat my dinner." It was a favorite phrase. Once he added: "If you want to eat peacock tongues, you can have them at home."

"So could you," said Lucullus, "if you ever came to dine with me."

"Thanks, I'll stay here where I can keep Syrian swine out."

"Each to his taste," laughed Lucullus. "I've met Roman swine in this house."

He meant Publius Clodius, of course, a man Lucullus did not exactly love.

And yet my uncle had traits not without a claim to admiration. His reputation as a harsh creditor was qualified by one thing: He never overreached anyone. He never lied. He never touched dirty money.

He never lent money on the prospect of an inheritance. He

11

never subsidized a scheme of fraud. His investments were simple matters; bottomry loans on corn ships occasionally, but infrequently. Once he financed a Dionysiac troupe in Sicily. That was rather to oblige Metellus, a sort of kinsman since he was a clansman. It happened only once. My uncle used to chuckle over the fact that Metellus lost money on it, but he did not. It was the only kind of thing that did elicit a chuckle from him.

As a matter of fact, he could have been much richer than he was. Indeed, if he had chosen, since he was no extravagant voluptuary like Lucullus, nor an unscrupulous politician like Marcus Crassus, he might have been richer than either, by doing as they did and hundreds of others of their class and ours. One source of wealth in those days he never used. He would take no blood money. I am glad to say I was never tempted to.

By blood money I mean money made by buying at auction the confiscated property of the victims of the Terror. Estates went cheap in the days of Sulla. His favorites wanted cash, not land or slaves—at any rate, not farm slaves. One picked up rare bargains in the Forum in the days after the slaughter on that dreadful November, exactly forty-nine years ago today. I was in Epirus, and my agent in Rome, my freedman Athamas, never forgave me for forbidding him to bid. "After all," he said quite rightly, "the proscribed men are dead anyway. You do them no good by letting the gang of Chrysogonus get the pickings." But neither I nor my uncle appeared at the public sales. Whether he abstained from squeamishness or prudence I am not sure. He said it was prudence. He was right in foreseeing Cato's investigations and Caesar's later attempt at expropriating the expropriators, but I believe he was better than he claimed to be. It was not a decent way to become rich.

Nor did he buy shares in the tax-farming societies. And that

12

surely was not for love of the provincials whom the publicans oppressed. No, he simply did not like it. The profits lay too much in buying governors and juries, in feeing informers and hiring thugs. With all his professed contempt for patriotism and public business, he hated all the things that made Rome a nightmare in the days after Sulla; or during Sulla's rule, for that matter. I think he would have loved his country if his country had in his time been more lovable.

I have followed his precepts in many respects. My father died when I was scarcely twenty. For those days, I found myself more than well-to-do. My uncle's methods seemed to me the most reasonable, if I wished to increase my wealth. And I did wish it. Let my Stoic friends lick their chops over that.

Like my uncle, I made certain rules and adhered to them. I venture to say that my rules were better, if for nothing else than the rate of interest which I charged. He never took less than one per cent a month. I frequently took half that, and generally two-thirds. I hope I showed more courtesy to my clients than he did. But in one respect I was unyielding. I did not renew. If the terms had been agreed upon, they must be followed. I insisted on having the time of payment kept.

And I also hope the use I made of my money was somewhat more befitting a Roman and a man of humane education. If my uncle ever made a present, it has escaped all record. I don't believe he ever did; not a denarius. He gave presents to us, his family, on festive occasions, but that was rather the usual sort of exchange among kinsmen. Our presents to him were—I do not boast of it—richer than his to us.

Certainly I will not be charged with remissness here. I have always been ready to give without expectation of return, where need was. I have had my favorites in this, as the world knows. If I have preferred the city of Athens to other communities, it

13

is a gesture of gratitude. Our Master, Epicurus, was an Athenian. At Athens, I enjoyed the loftiest and most stirring exaltation of which I believe any man is capable. To be sure, my feet never left the rocky soil of the city. My Pythagorean friends under similar circumstances would doubtless have been halfway to the empyrean.

And to Athens I have been generous. If effusive gratitude is a proof, I have been too generous. But I don't really think so. Athenians are lively and sprightly persons, likely to say "Thank you, a thousand times" when once would be enough. To read an honorary inscription at Athens is to learn how much can be made of very moderate services. Until I left Athens, just before Cicero's consulship, I would not let them put up statues in my honor. They have a considerable collection of them now. I am not proud of them as works of art.

Perhaps it was rather the opportuneness of my services than their quantity which gave them their value. When Sulla left Athens, it could not have been picked cleaner of transportable booty than if it had been cleared for migration. I gave them no money, but I lent it to them. Evidently I could not have given them as much as I could lend or cause to be lent to them. I charged no interest except what I had to pay to those to whom I pledged my credit. And here, as always, I announced that I would not renew. They had three years to pay.

That I helped them feed their citizens from time to time is something I hardly deserve credit for. It was an emergency. One does not see men starve with whom one has lived as long as I lived with my Athenians.

I have helped others in exactly the same way. Evidently I did not always say "Yes" to the demands made on me. I should have needed the touch of Midas to have satisfied everybody.

14

Even Marcus Cicero, the man who could properly ask most of me, asked too much at times. Doubtless he thought me luke-warm when I declined to lend him all that he asked, declined to throw all my fortunes into the scale that he pointed out. I think I gave at the right time and that I gave the right amount. Perhaps, as he believed, I could have bought off some of Clodius' pack. Doubtless Clodius himself might have been had for a price. But I knew too well that Caesar meant to discipline Marcus and that he intended—since Marcus would take no hint—to make him feel his fist. The money would have been wasted. I did not stint my funds when Cicero returned in what was almost a triumphal procession through Italy.

Few can know how difficult it was to resist the pressure that was put upon me. One thing, however, I had determined. I was not to be pushed into politics by my wealth, when I could not be pushed into it by ambition. And how they all played on me! "A hundred talents down now, and you can make what terms you will with the conqueror." It was only necessary to put in the place of the word "conqueror," "Cinna," "Caesar," "Pom-peius," "Antonius," "Cassius," "Sextus," and the sentence tells the song that was dinned in my ears so often, in the tumultuous years in which my life has been spent. "A hundred talents can buy ships and men and provisions." "A hundred talents will give us credit for four hundred more." I remained deaf to all of them. Over and over again, I was warned that in the state of affairs at Rome there was no middle course. You must be for a man or against him.

Well, I have kept a middle course as far as the contestants for power were concerned. And I am still here in my house on the Quirinal, that was once the house of my uncle Quintus. To be sure, I shall quit it soon, but it will not be because Caesar rather than Antonius, or Antonius rather than Caesar, will be the master of the state. It will be an acute indigestion rather than an armed centurion who will turn me out of my house.

And if I steered a middle course, it was not because I had no political beliefs or because I concealed them. I was still within the age of the Edict when I discovered for myself that I must separate from the party of the Gracchans and of Marius, the party of my father and his friends. Rome has never been a democracy. I saw no prospect that it could be one. My reasoned conviction put me on the side of Sulla and the aristocratic theory of government. I avowed these views openly when the older Lepidus filled the city with riot and rapine, while his followers roared, "Down with the oligarchs! Down with the Sullan tyranny!" I did not pretend to change when Caesar and the scamp Publius declared that the city rabble was the Roman people, nor when Pompeius and his senators were scurrying with breakneck speed to the Adriatic ports out of the way of the Gallic legions.

I neither helped nor hindered the removal of Gaius Caesar, but I approved the short-lived attempt of Brutus to re-establish the senatorial government. However, I had no intention of becoming the Treasurer of the Liberators. They took it hard. Marcus Brutus, whose temper was always bad, snarled that if I would not join the group that was being formed to finance the state, I should have only myself to thank if I found how easily they could dispense with me. I was not offended.

For all his anger, Brutus was glad enough to accept my help when the scheme broke down and it behooved him to leave Italy to the Caesarians, rather more precipitously than became a praetor of the Roman people. He never quite forgave me. That is one of the difficulties with philosophical eclectics. They have so many principles that they act as though they had none.

16

It was a pity about Marcus Brutus. Cicero and I tried to make a Scipio Aemilian out of him. He did not possess the stuff that was needed. There was a man with whom we might have been more successful, out of whom something better than Scipio might have been made. That was Marcus Cato. If only he had been taught a better way of life than the inhumane and unnatural doctrine of the Porch.

III

TO HAVE LIVED so long in surroundings of such violence, among men so eager, so powerful, so forceful, and so passionate, means to have lived dangerously. On more than one occasion, I know, but for the active intervention of some person, I should have suffered the fate of so many others. It is curious that those who intervened were men who ordinarily had no hesitation in sacrificing their friends to gratify their ambitions, and were the sort of people to whom half-hearted adherence—they would always call my adherence half-hearted —was worse than none. Marcus Cicero's delay in joining Pompeius—and it was the most excusable of delays—was enough to make all the Pompeians, and Gnaeus himself, regard him as little better than an enemy. Nor ought Marcus really to have complained of that. In his furious struggles with Clodius and with Antonius he was continually upbraiding me and everybody else with lack of ardor. "To hesitate in such things," he kept repeating, "is to declare yourself on the other side."

Why did these men spare me? If they wanted my property— and they did want it—I could not have protected it against them. A file of soldiers could have ejected me from the

Quirinal and a single battalion of mercenaries might have occupied my estates in Epirus. Whatever I possessed in actual money and art treasures—I had nothing else worth taking—could have been seized in an hour. Yet I cannot complain that anything like this happened to me. No one ever laid violent hands on me or mine.

One of the ablest men I knew was Gaius Cassius, less a friend, perhaps, than most of those I have named. When I refused to join the consortium of bankers for the Liberators, Marcus Brutus was not the only one who scowled. In fact the proposal was made among them—the suggestion came from Trebonius, I was told—to give me a choice between voluntary adhesion and confiscation. That was called a choice more than once, in my memory. Marcus Brutus offered no objection. It was Cassius who prevented it.

He came especially to tell me of it. "You will, of course, be eternally grateful," he said, smiling at me with his puckered lips, and stroking his sharp chin, "I warned our friends that applying the screws to you might be a little harder than they thought. I am not completely convinced that the Romans appreciate as thoroughly as they should the benefit we have conferred on them by the execution of the tyrant. And among those who do not appreciate it, there are many who do appreciate you, Titus Pomponius—you, and the incalculable convenience of a banker who is apparently untroubled by revolutions, who charges moderate interest, and who is," he bowed, "notoriously solvent. I should be glad to enter into a set of reciprocal stipulations with the Caesarians, with the Parthians, with the Gauls and the Spaniards, that, whatever else happens, no one must disturb the tablets of Quintus Caecilius' nephew."

"That may prove insufficient security," I said, "if the pressure becomes very hard."

19

"What do you call really hard pressure?" asked Cassius.

"One of two things: an armed soldier, or the urgent need of a friend."

Cassius smiled. "I understand you. And I think I have made Marcus and Decimus understand."

I found ships and sailors for both Marcus Brutus and Cassius only a few months later. And a letter to my agent at Rhodes.

Cassius certainly was right in part. It was something to know where money could be obtained without violence, and at less than one per cent. I did not refuse aid to the Liberators when they abandoned Italy. Nor did I surrender the family of Antonius a little later to the vengeance even of Marcus Cicero and the Senatorial Commission.

Fulvia had only herself to thank that she was hated. There were three reasons for hating her: her first husband, Publius Clodius, her second husband Marcus Antonius, and above all, herself. We are not used to women in politics at Rome—at any rate, openly in politics. We don't like them. These Macedonian viragos, these Berenices and Cleopatras, and Arsinoës and Stratonices, who have been setting the East by the ears ever since Alexander died, they give us a little shiver of repulsion. And we don't like women strutting about as Fulvia did after the Liberators had left Italy and Antonius took on the airs of being the rightful successor of Caesar as, legally, he doubtless was. Above all, we don't like women in military uniform, and Fulvia, dressed in helmet and cuirass with a Spanish sword dangling on her right hip, was not a pleasing spectacle, for all her fine looks. Perhaps because of her fine looks. But, of course, that was a later manifestation.

A great many things that Marcus Cicero said of her in his speeches were not true. Yet enough was true to make Rome gasp and the Senate foam with rage.

20

Then came the news from Mutina. Marcus Antonius was defeated. Some said he was killed. At any rate, he was in flight to the north, where Hirtius or young Caesar or Decimus Brutus would overtake him in a day. We did not know then that Hirtius was dying of his wounds. But wherever Antonius was, he was crushed and the Commission of Ten and Cicero were ready to wreak vengeance on his family.

It was touch and go whether Fulvia and her children would be executed. Quintus Fufius, in whose house they lived, told them he could no longer protect them. The poor man was in mortal terror. I can hardly blame him. I never saw a person so relieved as he was when I told him that the family could come to me at the Quirinal.

Cicero was extremely angry with me, not for the first time. But I carried my point. Fulvia and her children were safe from personal molestation on the Quirinal, as I knew they would be. I had a harder task to prevent the confiscation of their property. After all, Antonius had been declared a public enemy.

The Commission did not insist on it. Our law does not impose penalties on the families of criminals, as so many states still do. I venture to think, however, that it was less compunction about the law than my intervention that changed their minds. I did not escape sharp censure. Even Marcus in an outburst of indignation declared I was guarding against a possible return of Antonius to power. I should have been possessed of greater skill in prophecy than I could boast, to have foreseen such a contingency. I don't believe that this consideration played a part. I think I acted as our Master, Epicurus, would have acted. Marcus' intemperance I could well discount. He had personal reasons to hate Fulvia which the rest of us did not have.

And Marcus, to do him justice, had no share in the petty

persecution that so many of our party took refuge in, when their first attempt failed. He did not support the fifteen or twenty law-suits that were instituted against Fulvia, mostly on the theory that she had helped Antonius embezzle state funds. They came to nothing, partly at least, because I supplied her with funds to defend herself.

She was a difficult guest, much more so than the others who were with her in my house. Far more so than my friend Volumnius. Volumnius, I suppose, was fair game. He was an active partisan, he was rich, and he had an incurable tendency to mockery. He might well have expected to suffer the fate of his leader. It is likely that he escaped because, till after the first flush of vindictive passion had subsided, no one knew he was at my house.

Indeed, it was to Volumnius for whom I did little, rather than to Fulvia for whom I did much, that I owed my life at the only time when it was imminently threatened.

Octavian joined Antonius, and affairs took their sudden swing against the Senate. Some of us, who remembered Caesar after the flight of Pompeius, had for a moment a surging hope that there would be an amnesty. What we got was the Terror.

I do not like to think of the horror of those days. They seared our souls. And yet there were bright spots. When the wolves came down to Rome with their lists, when every wall had notices of rewards for treason and murder, there were slaves who let themselves be cut down on behalf of their masters, and men and women who sacrificed their property and their lives in what was often a fruitless effort to save their friends and kinsmen. But for these things, I should have despaired not only of the republic but of the human race. That Volumnius harbored me, my wife and my child, while the assassins were roaming through the streets to kill and pillage, was a real risk for him. He turned it off with a jest, as he would. "Who would hesitate," he said, *"e tenebris tantis tam clarum extollere lumen?"* Even my poor Lucretius, who had everything that an Epicurean should have, except a sense of humor, would have been gratified that men quoted him as Greeks might quote Homer.

Of course, when Antonius arrived I was safe. He told me that in all the proposed lists of men to be proscribed it had never occurred to anyone to include my name. That may have been gratitude for my efforts for his family. I do not know. I did my best to intercede for the Ciceros. It was too late. Even if it had not been, I should not have succeeded.

"I could have forgiven him anything he ever said," Antonius declared to me at his house, "except his slurs on my Latin. What, had the man not read my masterly treatise 'On the Art of Being Drunk'?" There was a yell of laughter among the fawning crowd around him. The strange thing is that Antonius really thinks he can write and that the Asianic fustian he has published will outlive Cicero.

Marcus Cicero's was a rich and passionate nature. He was also a keen and shrewd judge of men even if he did not always act on his judgment. And above everything else he loved the Rome we both created out of the traditions of our history and the hopes we had for the future, when we were boys together in school. He loved this Rome well enough to die for it. His gifts of mind were so much greater than mine that they were beyond jealousy. His friendship was very precious to me. When he was killed, I found consolation in my family, my books, my collections, and, more than all else, in the guidance of my Master. I am not ashamed to add that I also found it in my fortune.

This fortune of mine—much depleted now, of course—will

23

soon be in the hands of others. What they will do with it I cannot tell, and I should not wish to determine even if I thought I could. Most of it will go to my daughter, and be administered therefore by her husband. That is some guaranty that it will be well used, although I have not been able to persuade Agrippa to adopt the way of Epicurus. That would have been a triumph.

I wonder who it was who first affected to despise wealth. Evidently it is an affectation. It is as though a man should despise food or clothing, or a soldier despise his sword or shield, or a peasant despise his plough. I know that there are Epicureans who pretend to be indifferent to wealth and who will boast of the frugality and simplicity of their lives. I should say that simplicity by itself has as little value as extravagance. Wealth is power, of course. It has always been so. I do not know of any community in which wealth has not counted even for the gratification of political ambitions. My Athenians tried for a time to make poor and rich exactly alike by drawing lots for political offices. And the Spartans attempted to prevent wealth from being accumulated by devices like iron money and the prohibition of imports. These things did not last. They never really worked even while they were supposed to be in operation.

The Cynics and the Stoics preach much about the contempt of riches. I find it hard to talk to Stoics except when they take a temporary vacation from their Stoicism. With Cynics conversation is a little easier. But, of Stoics or Cynics both, their attitude of lofty superiority is based on so many different things that I get a little puzzled. "A man is to be valued for what he is and not for what he has," is Stoic doctrine, I think. And my recent guest, Menippus, is fond of repeating the Cynic formula that a rich man does not possess riches but is possessed by them.

That is all very fine, but it does not quite make sense. I do not understand what they mean when they say a rich man is

24

not better than a poor man. He certainly lives better, and that is a form of being. He is safer, more powerful, generally much cleaner and, on the whole, healthier. At any rate, he can be healthier if he wishes to. He can acquire more learning and wider experience. That ought to mean that he can be wiser. His wealth will not make him stronger or braver or taller—perhaps not even handsomer, although fine feathers are nearer to making fine birds than we admit.

And, of course, riches will not make him kinder to those he loves. But since Stoics despise kindness and love as they despise wealth, this cannot be what they mean.

As far as I can disentangle their notions, it is that a poor man ought not to be required to revere or obey a rich man merely for his wealth. Quite so. But no man should be required to venerate or obey another for any reason, if he does not do so of his own impulses.

For my part, I have liked the sensation of being rich. I have liked to feel that most of the things I wanted I might have. If I had been seriously limited in this respect, I cannot see how my mind could have escaped becoming narrowed and restricted and less capable of its fullest growth.

I do not mean that I have been able to satisfy every whim or caprice the moment it arose in me. That is not the way we live in our fellowship of the Garden. Whims are the shifting winds of impulse that may take us over a precipice as well as along the road we have marked for ourselves. There is nothing either good or bad about an impulse. The question is always what it results in.

I do not consider it a limitation that my wealth, ample as it was, was far less than I should have needed if I had attempted to build palaces at Baiae and at Tarentum or to spend a hundred thousand sesterces on a single banquet. I did not feel

25

restricted because I could not have these things. I did not want them. I can't see why anybody should have wanted them. I have been a guest at banquets in gold and marble and ivory palaces and I have been bored. Not more bored, I fancy, than my host was.

I never quite understood Lucullus, who was my uncle's friend and mine. He was a man of real capacity. I do not believe that his extravagance was mere ostentation. Ostentation can have only one purpose—of exciting envy, or, rather, a kind of envious hatred. I can't see how men can wish to be hated, although I suppose some may have wished, and still wish, to be feared. There must be some satisfaction in it. I have seen brute beasts elated over the terror they inspire in weaker animals. Barbarous tribes in the German forests, Caesar the Dictator wrote in his book, take a ferocious pride in the fact that no other tribe dares dwell near them.

But even this brutal and barbarian satisfaction is wanting here. The display of wealth does not inspire fear. It does enable a man to collect about him hundreds who will praise him to his face if he can endure that sort of gratification. Surely it is the poorest and thinnest sense of superiority that is confirmed by the attendance of parasites and flatterers. Of these there were enough at Lucullus' tables, and it is impossible to believe that he actually derived any pleasure from their presence. He took, it is true, a malicious delight in stimulating them to more and more extravagant expressions, but this amusement must soon have worn out. I confess I cannot make it out.

If he had been an unsavory rascal like Publius Vedius or Menas, grown rich by fraud and proscriptions, it would be easy enough to understand. A man whose back still shows scars enough of the lash to remind him and us how recently he was a peculiarly worthless sort of slave, might think that gorgeousness and lavishness are marks of belonging to the upper classes. In men like that, to be regarded as a member of the upper classes is a persistent craving. It is the only way persons without imagination can build up a sense of self-respect for themselves.

Is it the absurd ostentation of wealth by Vedius or Menas or by any other plundering ruffian who wriggled through war and massacre with other men's goods in his possession—is it this which makes Stoics and Cynics think that riches are despicable? If it is, it does not speak well for their common sense. Money purchases so many things which one needs, it makes so many choices possible, that it deserves effort to acquire and care in husbanding.

My wealth has served me well. I hope it will be as useful to Marcus Agrippa.

IV

THE THOUGHT OF next year oppresses me. It is so un-likely that I shall live to see it that it seems like an event of a distant and remote future, something in that posterity for whose approval so many thousands strain every nerve and with which they can have as little contact as with Romulus or with Numa. But my darling Atticula will see it, and Agrippa and Nepos, and my freedman Quintus, and Alexis, who has served me so well and so long. He, too, will be free then. My will provides it. He could have been free long ago if he had wished it.

I suppose if I doctored myself continuously I might painfully drag out the months until the decision is reached between the two rivals for the lordship of the world. It may take much longer than a few months. The struggle may last years, and if it does, there will be little enough left of Roman blood or Italian sinew in the world. How shrill their exultation will be—the Gauls, the Germans, the Spaniards, the Moors, the Parthians, the Egyptians, the Scythians—as they sweep down upon our Italy after we have so conveniently slaughtered each other for their benefit.

28

I know that my fellow Epicureans will shake their heads. "Suppose it is so. Suppose Rome really falls a victim to her own fratricidal madness. Suppose swarthy Libyans and shaggy and filthy Hercynians trample down the waving cornfields of your Campanian estates and pull apart your Corinthian carvings. What difference will it make to you, who will be dead? Have you forgotten the Master's words? Or the chants you love so much, of your friend Titus, the book you have read so often, and have heard even oftener? Must you always, like a half-trained boy, be reminded that you cannot at the same time be dead and be alive? If these things happen next year or the year after, when you will have been duly placed upon the pyre, duly bewailed and decently and piously deposited in the tomb on the Appian Way, one thing is certain: these portentous events will not be happening to you. That those you love will suffer under them is sad. But it will not be your sadness, but theirs. You cannot really share it; nor, indeed, for all your sympathetic effort, really understand it. You did not, after all, die when young Marius died, nor when Cicero died, nor when Pillia died. And if your daughter in the anarchy you foresee should be dragged off as the booty of a swinish and half-human pirate, believe me, your sleep will not be troubled by that horror for one little instant."

That is the hardest of the demands that our doctrine makes upon me. Fear of death I have never known, nor of anything that lies beyond death. That at a definite moment I shall cease to breathe and think, and that then I shall be as though I never was—this I know, as certainly as I know anything. But it is hard to remember that, deeply as I have attached myself to others in my long life, they became no part of me, nor I of them. I have taught myself so long to believe that their grief was my grief, so long rejoiced in what pleased and delighted

29

them, that it is difficult to realize that in a short time this will not be so, and that I shall soon have no share in their concerns because I shall have vanished altogether as a thinking and feeling person. During my Pillia's long illness I could see the changes in her body and feel with her, in some degree, the pains she endured. I cannot feel them, nor see her wasted face, now that she is dead, and my bereavement and the loss of her society she cannot feel at all. It will evidently not be otherwise for me and my Atticula, merely because it is I who will then be beyond pain or feeling and she the one to be bereaved.

All this I tell myself frequently, but it does not quite remove the sense of dread with which I foolishly contemplate what may happen if the next ten years are as full of civil war as the last fifteen have been. And, of course, what I dread may not happen at all. A single battle may be as decisive as Pharsalus.

We do not believe in Fate, we Epicureans. Of the silly stories the poets tell, none is sillier than that of the three hags who spin out our thread of life, measure it off and snip it, with, I suppose, adamantine shears. And all in accordance with specific decrees, made no one knows when. For my part, I have no better opinion of the little old lady whom the Stoics call Providence and who sits on the shoulder—or perhaps within the heart—of Father Jupiter and tells him what to do.

No, the events of the world are not fixed. One thing may happen as well as another. The only purpose in the world is that which men bring into it. With good will, men could make life pleasant in the years I shall not see. By reckless yielding to their passions and their greed they can make it horrible. The world can be moulded. I hope it will be moulded by Caesar and Agrippa and Maecenas, rather than by Antonius and his royal Egyptian harlot. It would have been better, of course, if it had been moulded by men like Scipio and Cicero and Cato;

but the task needed qualities they did not possess. I am inclined to think that Caesar has not wholly forgotten or disregarded the lessons he received when he first came to Rome, from Marcus Cicero.

If Caesar is victorious my forebodings will have been vain enough and the lives of those I cherish will be easy and pleasant and comfortable. At least I can hope that with some confidence. Ultimately, of course, they too will disappear. They will be outlived by this house, by the trees I myself planted, by the trees that were here before my uncle lived here. And even these will be outlived by what I see around me while I am dictating these words to Dionysius: the bronze and marble and silver and gold statues and ornaments with which I have relieved the rustic severity that my uncle preferred.

They will be scattered soon, I suppose, but they will be here for a time to be looked at and appreciated by Agrippa's guests. It is a little sad to contemplate how much more lasting the brass and marble and gold are than the living men for whom they were put into beautiful shapes.

Shall I confess that it grieves me to relinquish them? There is that exquisite silver cup that I bought from Agatharchides at Samos. It has nothing on it but a dappled fawn cropping the grass beneath a maple. There is a frieze of ivy leaves running under the brim. I do not know the artist. I should say it is Sicyonian of some time before Aratus. It has a harmony of line and a grace of form that seem to me unequaled. There could not have been a movement of the designer's finger or his hammer that was out of control. That is why, I suppose, it gives me so much pleasure.

Indeed, I enjoy the smaller objects I have gathered somewhat more than the larger and more magnificent ones. These too, however, give me abundant satisfaction. I have the Eros of

Praxiteles which Verres took from Messana and which I bought from Lucius Antonius, who must have got it from his brother, after Verres had been proscribed and killed. But I would give all that Praxiteles ever made for my two athletes by Polyclitus or the bronze hoplite of Calamis. And into the western wall of my atrium on the Quirinal I have fitted two paintings by Apelles. One represents Circe shrinking from the moly in the hand of Odysseus, and the other the sacrifice of Iphigenia. They are a subtle and a constantly renewed pleasure.

I have never thrown my house open to the public. Other men have done so, and my refusal has confirmed in people's minds a certain repute for miserliness which I do not think I quite deserve. My friends were welcome to enjoy with me what I enjoyed, so far as they were able.

They were not all able. It needs a special sensitiveness to get from a carved gold inlay or a heroic bronze what it really contains. I have this capacity in some measure. Cicero had it much less than I did. It amazes me to realize that the Roman who in my experience had it most fully was Gaius Verres, who in other respects was as vicious and cruel a rascal as any I ever saw.

You would scarcely have supposed, to look at Verres' round, flat, and pudgy face, his thick neck, his little blinking eyes, that he had the soul of an artist. Yet despite Marcus Cicero's malicious sneers it was he and not his Greek stewards who put together the most splendid collection of art treasures that any of us ever knew. Verres had an eye so keen that he could see at once minute variations in the curve of a sculptured arm which became evident to me only after careful examination. He was nothing less than a voluptuary in his love of color and form, and I fully believed his statement that he felt a physical shiver when he first saw the Hermes at Tyndaris. He meant to compliment me when he said: "You will understand me, Titus

32

Pomponius, if the rest of my countrymen do not. I speak as one expert to another." He did me too much honor to rank me with him. I was far his inferior in knowledge and appreciation of such matters, although almost his equal in love of them. I am convinced, however, that even if I had been as tempted as he was, I should have declined to acquire his treasures in the way in which he did. I never knew a man so completely devoid of any feeling of common humanity. He was quite capable of crucifying a provincial—Marcus says he did—for a Pergamene tapestry. Men like that profoundly repel me. I could understand why my distant kinsman, Quintus Caecilius, attempted to save him by a rather underhanded trick. Caecilius was his quaestor and owed him loyalty. But how so urbane and high-minded a person as Quintus Hortensius could have openly defended him and received him at his house, I cannot understand. I suppose politics accounts for it. I think Hortensius was ashamed of it, later.

Those who moralize on the vicissitudes of fortune have dwelt on the fact that Verres and Cicero, who hated each other so intensely, died within a month of each other, slain by the order of the same man and victims of the same proscription. They died equally bravely, too. I am afraid these coincidences do not impress me as much as they do others. In themselves events are meaningless enough, and their similarities or contrasts are hardly worth noticing.

I have tried hard not to remember that many of the things which give me so much pleasure to see and touch are also rare things which cost a great deal of money. Not altogether successfully. I am enough my uncle's nephew to know exactly what I have paid for everything I possess. To be sure, I have a great many inexpensive modern vases and reliefs made by men I know, like Arcesilaus of Cyrene. I confess I have little patience with our fashionable sculptor, Pasiteles, whose dull imitations I brush against in the house of every third Roman of my acquaintance. And I have picked up in cities of Asia and Syria and Greece and Italy a large number of little bits of craftsmanship that most of my contemporaries would disdain, partly because the makers are unknown, and partly, I fear, because the things were cheap.

It hardly becomes me, however, to be too disdainful of those who value things by their price. I showed Gnaeus Manlius a carved sapphire, the work of Leonidas, and boasted that it was unique in its kind and that it cost twenty thousand sesterces. He offered me twenty-five, which I refused, but I had to endure the jibes of Maecenas and Quintus Horatius, who were my guests at the time, and who kept up a continual fire of banter on the subject. Whatever they saw—the commonest piece of furniture—Maecenas gravely asked Quintus what he supposed it was worth, and after mentioning an absurd sum they would utter a joint "Ah!" of admiration.

Maecenas, as a matter of fact, is a man of taste. From time to time he calls himself one of us. I should not like to question him on doctrine, but he is the most delightful of companions, and this young Apulian poet from whom he is inseparable has greater skill than Catullus. He is just the age now at which Catullus died. He lacks, of course, the intensity and vigor and courage and sweep of Catullus, but we may be sure he will not waste his strength as Catullus did in desperate debauches. He also professes to be of our fellowship, and Statilius, our learned young doctor and mentor, assures me that he is well grounded but that his conduct is deplorably loose. I wish Statilius might himself learn to combine with his knowledge and the austerity of his life something of the gaiety and ease of the Teacher whose writings he so profoundly analyzes.

34

Certainly no Epicurean can assert that rarity and expensiveness make objects beautiful or desirable. But when they are beautiful for other reasons, does the fact that they are rare and correspondingly dear really count for nothing in our estimation of them? I cannot get rid of the feeling that it does count for something, although I cannot justify it by anything in reason or in the doctrine of our Master. Perhaps at the back of our minds is the thought that what is rare has a precarious existence. If it is lost it cannot be replaced. That is not satisfactory, clearly. All works of art are unique. We are still laughing at Lucius Mummius a hundred years after his death because he warned the shipmasters who transported the statues from Corinth that if the cargo was lost they would have to replace it.

No, I cannot account for the satisfaction I have in the fact that so many of my treasures are like nothing else that any other collector has, and that they could be sold for the value of hundreds of acres of cornland. Any other collector! It is lucky that Volumnius does not hear me, or young Horatius.

From my garden I can see to the north the magnificent park that Lucullus constructed. Still closer to me is the series of parks and villas of Gaius Sallustius, who died only two years ago. His grand-nephew who is his adopted son lives there now, an inoffensive and, I am told, an able young man. At least he does not have to explain how a moralizing historian can attack the plunderers of provinces in his books and pillage provinces ruthlessly himself when he is given the opportunity. Sallustius was my neighbor for ten years. We never visited each other.

And to the south I can see the weathered gilt of the Capitolium on the sacred hill. Caesar talks of rebuilding it—above all, of getting a better group of Jupiter and his four-horsed chariot for the acroterium. Twenty years ago, anyone who had such a plan would have written to me at Athens or Buthrotum

35

to find a suitable group or a competent artist. When Gnaeus Pompeius built his theater, he asked me to get him statues to put up in it. Cicero was continually commissioning me to provide him with pictures and vases and statues for his villas and his house. I wish he had commissioned me exclusively. Some of the things he got from Caelius for the Tusculanum did not go well with what I sent him. Harmony of combination was his greatest difficulty. Indeed he was a little less competent in all matters of art than many men far inferior to him. Every now and then he would pose as the ancient Roman who scorned all this Greek nonsense, as he did in the attack on Verres which he published but never delivered. We laughed him out of this affectation. Indeed, it was never taken seriously, even by the people for whom those speeches were intended.

In this, as in other things, Marcus went beyond what the conventions of public oratory demanded. To pretend to have heard of Praxiteles only just before he prepared his speech, to need a reminder of who or what Myron was, or Polyclitus, was almost indecent jesting. In fact, in the history of art, in the names and the rank of the artists, Cicero's unusual powers of memory gave him a great advantage, and his quickness and resourcefulness enabled him to take part in discussions of art better than men who had more native taste and more precise judgment.

I have acquired no small learning in this field. And it has its value, not merely for one who wishes to collect, but for one who wishes to understand. I should be a little ashamed, after so many years of active interest, not to be able to tell a copy from an original, a forgery from a genuine work. That is a matter, to be sure, in which one needs to know a great many external facts about the artist and about his work, a knowledge that could be possessed by men without any interest in these things except as merchandise. But it also helps to quicken the eye in seeing them as beautiful objects, and it stimulates a love for them, to let our minds dwell on these incidental things and thus see works of art in a dozen lights rather than in one alone. I have wrangled pleasantly with Salvius over the attribution of an ancient marble relief of mine. I think it is earlier than the Persian wars. Salvius thinks it is a generation later. We shall certainly not come to an agreement on it in my lifetime. I don't think we ever wanted to come to an agreement on it.

Smoothness, grace, richness, harmony, accuracy, these are things which most of us have looked for in determining whether a work of art is lovely or not. I wonder whether these qualities are as important as I have been inclined to deem them. In my later years I have been fascinated by what we were taught in school to regard as the rude beginnings of art, beginnings which were to culminate in the glorious period of Praxiteles and Alcamenes. Were they really beginnings, or were they self-sufficient expressions? Or rather, did artists move in the wrong direction after Calamis and Myron? It is something worth pondering.

In my ring cabinet the place of honor is not given to the marvel of golden artistry which King Antiochus sold me, but to the signet ring of my father. It would be entitled to this place as a mark of piety, of course. But, as a matter of fact, there are few of my smaller treasures that I view with greater satisfaction. The stone is a simple carnelian, and the design an eagle, not a superb eagle with spreading wings like the obverse of the coins of Acragas, but a much ruder figure done with scarcely more than a dozen strokes. There is a kind of bold rigidity in it that recalls the figures of Canachus or the staring, smiling youths in the inner shrines of old Doric temples.

They tell me that archaic figures are becoming all the rage.

37

YOUNG MARCUS CICERO visited me last week, and for once he did not ask for money. Still more unusual, he stayed three days and was sober all the time. Tiro tells me he has not been really drunk for a month.

He was in fine fettle. He is a confirmed Caesarian now and eager for hostilities to commence so that he may wreak vengeance on Antonius in the name of Rome and of his father. Agrippa tells me that, if it should come to war, Marcus will get a legateship. He is a good soldier like his uncle Quintus, my brother-in-law.

Apparently, he is even a better soldier than Quintus. That is Agrippa's opinion, and there could hardly be a more competent judge. I confess I have had some doubt on the subject, but perhaps that is only jealousy on behalf of his father. The older Marcus would have been so proud of a little military glory. A little, to be sure, he really acquired in Cilicia, but mighty little! He was very self-conscious about it and rallied himself more than we rallied him about his mountain victory at Pandenissus—I think that was the name; I am ashamed to say that I have forgotten it again.

Well, it is no great matter. Nor was it a great victory. But it was quite as much a victory as some that earned other men the title of imperator. I can well believe that Marcus Cicero, the greatest master of speech of his day, heard the salutation of his soldiers, when the nest of brigands fell, with greater delight than the thunderous applause of the crowded Forum at the close of his most brilliant peroration. As I have said, I see no reason why he should not have added imperator to his name, as well as many another stormer of a mountain fort. And the letter Caesar addressed to him: "The Imperator Gaius Caesar to the Imperator Marcus Cicero"—perhaps it was irony, but I think not—at any rate, it was Marcus' proudest possession. It is quite true that Marcus had made something like a proverb of *cedant arma togae, concedat laurea laudi,* but, if the truth were told, deep in his heart, he lusted for the laurel.

So it is young Marcus, and not the old Marcus, who is to have a military reputation! I wonder whether he will really justify the hopes his new friends place in him. That young man has a way of disappointing expectations. How proud we were when he made his neat little speech on his coming of age! Every word his own, and no trick of style omitted! The older Marcus wept with delight. And I almost did, too.

Young Marcus has a quick and active mind. And a real feeling, I think, for literature. Besides, his manner is so ingratiating, when he wishes to be ingratiating, that the contrast between him and his cousin Quintus, my sister's son, was especially sharp. There was nothing ingratiating about young Quintus. At all times he was a graceless and sullen lad, selfish and bad-tempered. Little joy he ever brought to us, his father or his mother or his kinsmen. Perhaps I should say that he did not disappoint our expectations because we had none. In one thing, however, or rather in two, he did disappoint the expectations of

39

everybody. We none of us credited him with the depth of perfidy which made him willing to betray both Marcus and me to what he supposed was Caesar's anger. Nor, after this had happened, could we have guessed that the same young man would have been capable of immolating himself to save his father's life. Indeed, under the proscriptions, father and son vied with each other in the nobility of their deaths. Evidently it is not so easy to know everything about people, even when you have known them all their lives and even when their characters seem simple enough.

Of the four Ciceros there is only young Marcus left. It may well be that my feeling about him is quite wrong. He may outshine in the splendor of his rank his father and his ancestors. He is the son of a consul—and of what a consul! He may be consul, too. I hear that our Caesar has some such promotion in mind for him, partly as a challenge to Antonius, and partly, I hope, as slight compensation for the dreadful afternoon in Bononia when he surrendered his friend and master as the price of an alliance. Perhaps he could not help himself. I think I should have acted differently, since I rated friendship higher than Caesar Octavian did. But then, I could not be Caesar Octavian at all, either for good or ill.

I see Tiro often. There is no freedman in Rome, except my own Quintus—and he is something more than my freedman—who has more completely and unselfishly consecrated himself to the service of his patron's family and heritage. Young Marcus has always been a great trial to us. I can understand wild orgies and symposia. But why should Cicero's son have taken to solitary drinking? There was no austerity in Marcus the elder. He did not refuse himself to the pleasures of the table, of women, or of social intercourse. But he did these things moderately, as became a grown man and a trained mind. Nowhere in young

Marcus' intimate surroundings did he see an example of what Tiro tells me went on day after day at their house after Marcus returned from Spain. There is something peculiarly repellent in silent debauches. Far better the riotous extravagance of Caelius and his coterie.

But this, as Tiro tells me, has quite changed. Marcus has thrown himself eagerly into war and politics. He studies manuals of strategy and spends his leisure in reading and discussion. He has made a number of sensible and acute suggestions about his father's treatise on the state. At his last visit he said he might want to add an additional book to it, or perhaps write on the subject independently. If he does, I shall publish it. It cannot fail to be interesting.

All 'this, however, I fancy is rather expansiveness and temporary enthusiasm. In many respects young Marcus is still very young. But it vividly brought home to me an incident of almost a generation ago, when his father and I, seated on a terrace in my villa at Tarentum, discussed the boy's future, and Cicero planned a career for him that he admitted was to be a fusion of his own and mine. Young Marcus was to be a great orator, was to achieve the consulship early, and then, we hoped, would do what his father had not done, retire completely from public affairs to some villa or villas in Italy or Sicily or Greece and spend the rest of his life in the satisfactions which the love of books and the love of those who love books can give a man.

Neither of us, to be sure, had any confidence that we should live to see this picture made real. When we spoke of such things, the echoes of Sulla and Cinna and Lepidus were still ringing in our ears, and there was enough to foreshadow Milo and Clodius, Caesar and Pompeius. It was not a time at which one could safely assume that any person would escape the dangers which crowded about us and which had already been fatal to so many of the men we had known and loved. We were like men in a ship beset by storms, sufficiently sensible to know that our chances of reaching port were slight, but all the more passionately yearning for the safety and comfort of home. We spent more time than became us in imagining idyllic future happiness, if not for ourselves, at any rate for Marcus and Tullia and Atticula.

It is not so easy to change one's course of life at forty, as Cicero fancied his son would do and as he found himself unable to do. He might well have felt in his own blood and spirit how hard it would be. Brilliant success has its penalties. When we talked of all this, Cicero had just finished his consulship. He was fully accepted as a member of the senatorial party. Tullia, his darling, was Piso's wife, and Marcus Cato, whose approval we all valued more than that of any other man, had hailed him "father of his country." To look on life and society from this height and to decide reasonably and coolly and effectively to leave it and to return to what must seem a lower and less stirring level, to abandon deliberately the exhilaration of power and grandeur—no one of Cicero's temperament could have done that. He knew this well enough himself, as I knew it. That is why we preferred to imagine young Marcus doing it thirty, forty years hence.

Has anyone ever done what we planned for the boy? Sulla surely did not. Rome was still shaking with terror of him when he professed to leave the government in the hands of his lieutenants and devoted himself wholly to the enjoyment of his harlots and catamites. He never surrendered anything, really. And Lucullus equally cannot be said to have renounced glory in favor of a life of suavity and peace. He was an able soldier and a competent statesman, but he withdrew when his fortunes were at their ebb, not at their flood. Obviously, he would not consent to engage in a struggle for dominance. His outlook was quite too cynical for that. It amused him to see the old state fall apart, and he was even capable of egging the contestants on in a combat he had no mind to join. Of him also it must be said that he surrendered nothing when he became an expert in oysters and vintages and embroidered cloaks rather than in statecraft and strategy.

It is a hard emotion to trample down, the sense of self-importance which counts for so much in the desire for power and position. And there is no reason for subduing it if a man can get no satisfaction otherwise, provided he does not begrudge the price he has to pay. The price must be paid in full. A man cannot indulge the love of domination till it has carried him to the topmost heights and then dismiss it like a hired servant who has done his task and for whom he has no further work. It becomes too much for you, this impulse that has driven you so far and so splendidly, that has carried you where most men wish to arrive.

Cicero did not seriously suppose it could be otherwise. To be called "father of our fatherland" by Marcus Cato was like the sweet heady wine my friends make for me in Naxos. The taste remains forever on your lips and the fumes never altogether leave your brain. I was with Cicero in the theater when Aesopus played Accius' praetextan comedy of Brutus, and when the audience rose with a shout of approbation at the line *"Tullius qui libertatem civibus stabiliverat."* I don't recall how often the passage had to be repeated before the audience allowed the play to go on. Small wonder that his head swam. I, the sober and self-contained mentor at his side, was almost carried along with him. You cannot shake off things like that and order your life as though they had never happened.

In his candid moments Cicero knew that what made political

43

glory so intoxicating was the sense of personal supremacy and not the consciousness of serving his fellow men. I do not say that this last played no part. Love of human beings is a real thing. And love of one's fellow citizens must be as real. It is not merely real, but natural. To dislike them is, I am afraid, equally real, but not quite natural. There have undoubtedly been some men who hated their kind. My fellow Athenian, Timon, was, if the stories about him are true, a man like that. I do not quite believe them. The only explanation, I suppose, if the stories really are true, is that he was not quite sane. It was also said of my uncle Quintus that he was a misanthrope. That was not justified, and at all events my uncle did not play any of the strange pranks, which are credited to Timon, to show his hatred of men.

I should not say of myself, or of Marcus Cicero, or of most of the men with whom I lived all these years or with whom I live now, that we loved our fellow human beings just because they were men. There is, of course, a natural tendency to sympathy. I could not see a man suffer pain, not the lowest and most degraded man, not even a man whom I detested and feared, without some movement of participation. That people can feast their eyes on suffering—and I have known such persons—is a horrible thought. I do not like to see men suffer, even when they are deservedly punished. But I know there is no way of preventing suffering, as long as men are so constituted that their violent passions cannot be taught control, as long as war is one of the ordinary events of life. I should find it impossible to live at all if I thought about such things and nothing else. It would be a kind of madness. The only thing to do is to turn one's mind away from the sort of suffering which seems to be part of the way in which we live and do something, if it is possible, to lessen the pain that is unnecessary and undeserved.

44

Even here it is a very little that can be done. I do not think I should pass a stranger by who needed help, but I meet very few strangers. Those persons whom I do see, who are part of the life I have chosen for myself, I should give more than help if they needed it. I should actively try to prevent pain or harm from reaching them at all, or I should want to alleviate it if I could not prevent it. This I should do even though I rated them very differently; indeed, though in one way or in another my judgment of some of them was quite low. My affections are not determined by judgments of the ability or even of the character of those whom I know.

But I have neither affection nor dislike for the men I do not know. I have seen all sorts of persons from many remote parts of the world, sometimes in the streets of Rome and more often in the ports of Asia and Greece. Picturesque enough, some of them. That there is something loathsome and contemptible about barbarians, I never believed, and it is not true. There are men who say they are philosophers and disciples of Aristotle who will have it that their master taught this. I cannot find that in his books, if what the Peripatetics study are his books. And if it should be there, it would not mean a great deal to me. Our Master taught nothing like it.

But he did not teach that all men were alike, or that all groups were alike. There are peoples who have done more than others, and to think with pride upon achievements which not you but your fathers and grandfathers have accomplished is not a contemptible pride. I am not a little proud of being a Roman, although I have added little indeed to make future Romans proud of the generation of which I formed a part. I would not change to be an Athenian in blood as well as in citizenship. To be sure, it is absurd to speak of preferring what I could not alter, no matter how much I might try to alter it. But that I am

45

a Roman and not a Syrian, a Roman and not a Syracusan, a Gaul, or an Egyptian, fills me with a real satisfaction.

I cannot tell how much that satisfaction consists in the fact that my people have conquered these others, and that no one questions that Roman citizenship is a greater and more valuable thing than any other. I must confess I should be indignant if one who was not a Roman acted insolently toward me, more than if a Roman did so. It is not easy to discard the pride that comes of being a member of a dominant race.

I have made a real effort to discard pride so far as it includes a sense of superiority. After all, it was a member of a subject race, an Athenian—and even a colonial Athenian at that—who is the master and guide of my way of life. But it is idle to say that the stolid and unwashed Suabians, the thick-nosed, ugly Cappadocians, who furnish us our least valuable slaves, had, even when they were free of all control by Roman magistrates, anything a cultivated mind would desire or even a beggar would envy.

And thus once again I find myself boasting of my adherence to the company of Epicurus and yet expressing feelings that show my unfitness to belong to it. Perhaps that shows how essentially incapable we Romans are of philosophy; as incapable perhaps as Alexander and Pyrrhus were, who, both of them, had no lack of philosophic training and example, if not the best philosophic training. We smile somewhat loftily at the story of how Cineas reported to King Pyrrhus that our Senate was an assembly of kings. I never sat in that royal gathering, and I cannot, therefore, take the compliment to myself. But it pleases me none the less, just as, after one hundred and fifty years, whenever I read of the supercilious insolence of our Rhodian allies during the war with Perseus, I still feel part of the furious rage that I have no doubt my Caecilian and Pomponian forefathers felt.

I wonder whether national pride would have seemed so little a thing to our Master if he had lived in the days of Pericles and had been in the counsels of that Olympian. I raised the question with my friend and fellow Epicurean, Rabirius, but he is much more interested in the atoms and the construction of the universe than in what happens in our minds.

Philodemus will have an answer for me and, I am sure, an epigram to encase it in. He writes he is coming tomorrow. I have a shrewd suspicion that Atticula has written to him to come as soon as possible to persuade me to consult a new physician. I doubt whether we shall reach that topic at all.

VI

I GO OUT SO rarely now that it becomes something of an expedition. When I ordered my litter to be prepared a few days ago, my freedman Quintus raised his eyebrows. But he had the grace to say nothing of years and infirmities. I was no heavy burden for my four Paphlagonian bearers, I am sure; but I still managed to walk erect and without support when I left the litter, at Gaius Pollio's house.

There was much the same company as at the last time. And no one can deny that it was a distinguished group. There were Trebatius and Cascellius, Ofilius and Lucius Varius. Maecenas and Horatius did not come, this time; but young Vergilius was there. One would hardly have expected him to be absent when Pollio invited his friends to hear a new tragedy.

Of the dignitaries, I saw Messalla and Marcus Marcellus as well as Gnaeus Piso. From the corner of my eye I caught a glimpse of Silanus in a soft new toga that had a faint glow of amber in it, and at the right, toward the peristyle, there was, of course, Lucius Ateius; and equally of course, with him was the flashingly smiling Santra. He smiles just a little too much to suit me. Their dark skins stood out in marked contrast to the elegant paleness of Vergilius, who stood at Ateius' left.

In the place of honor—he could be nowhere else—sat Marcus Varro. Eighty-three years old he is, my senior by six years, and still plump and rosy for all his white hairs. As usual, Quintus Calenus, who never leaves him now, sat protectively near. Calenus is a silent and undemonstrative man. His father was a very different kind of person. I remember few things of him with pleasure except his capacity for sincere friendship. He gave the best demonstration of his devotion to Varro when he saved his life during the Terror.

He could not save his property. Not even his library. What Lucius and Marcus Antonius did with it, I cannot tell. Varro has not attempted to replace it. Pollio's books and mine are at his service.

Room was made for me at Varro's side. The younger men around him, senators most of them, praetorians and consulars some of them, rose to greet me. The deference was given, I know, to the father-in-law of Marcus Agrippa, not to the Roman knight or the rich banker.

Varro told me that he wanted me to look over his new treatise on the history of the Roman theater. When it is completed, it will make his seventieth work, and if, as planned, it runs into five books, his grand total of scrolls will exceed five hundred and ninety. That is a library in itself.

And then Pollio entered. On ordinary occasions he is very careful to be present when his guests arrive, and to greet them personally, but at these readings he does not come in till they are all assembled. There was a chorus of salutations, and Pollio bowed, smiling, and seated himself in the chair arranged for him, near the table where Agathon, his principal librarian and best copyist, had his scrolls ready.

49

I wish with all my heart that the manner and substance of the tragedy had been as novel as this whole notion of publicly reading your works to an assembly of invited guests. I am afraid I do not quite like it. Innovation for innovation, I am much more impressed with that other novelty of Pollio's, his fine public library open to all comers at seasonable times, with its portrait gallery of busts of Greek and Roman writers. It was a graceful compliment to include among them the head of our friend, Marcus Varro, the only living person to be so honored.

I confess I listened with only half an ear to Pollio's reading. He reads well. His gestures are few and simple. There is certainly nothing ridiculous in his writing an Antiope, nor in reading it. Still, I prefer the Antiope of Euripides. And, if I must be frank, even the fine old clumsy trimeters of Pacuvius on this well-worn theme. One can certainly not call Pollio's trimeters clumsy. These young men—I dare call a man of forty-five young, in the presence of Varro and of me—these young men have fluency and grace, no doubt about it. I like a little more savor and vigor.

Pollio went to Euripides rather than to Sophocles, this time, although on the whole he is inclined to prefer the latter. Horatius said his Niobe was worthy of its Sophoclean model. I am willing to wager that Pollio did not think so. Whatever one may say of him, one can hardly question his power of critical judgment.

Perhaps if he were not quite so critical in all respects he would now be contesting the mastery of the state with Antonius and Caesar. Or, more likely, he would have been swept away by one or the other of the calamities that destroyed so many men of force and personal vigor and spared so many critics and collectors of books and statues. Pollio is a critic of a different sort from me; for him, the things to examine are campaigns and

50

policies, not the styles of painters or the diction of poets, although he is by no means incompetent here, either. But his real impulse is in the other direction.

He has tasted what we Romans think is the supreme glory of men. He has ridden along the Holy Street in formal triumph, in Jupiter's chariot drawn by four white horses. His face was stained with the color of a god, his body clad in the purple robes of the Lord of Heaven and Earth. He ascended the Capitol to present to Jupiter the offerings of the conquering Romans. To be sure, he has enjoyed this vertiginous glory only once, not three times like Pompeius, or four like Caesar the Dictator. But once is more than falls to the lot of most men, even of most of our great men.

If he went up as a god, he came down as a sober and moderately discreet citizen. Caesar's officer who had found fault with Caesar's campaigns and questioned his good faith managed to break sharply with one of Caesar's successors and to hold aloof from the other. He has quarreled with Antonius, and, while he is on formally good terms with Octavian, he has not accepted an intimacy which I believe he might have had, although, obviously, not on his own terms. When I said that few men, if any, have voluntarily given up power to retire to the enjoyment of life, I meant Pollio among others. Pollio's career, in the state, triumphator though he was, was over. He is not capable of subordination.

Few persons have followed Pollio in this practice of public readings, although it has furnished a great deal of material for conversation and has occasioned more than one jibe. Vergilius has read for Pollio's guests and Varro's and my own. That was different. It was meant as a compliment to the young man and an occasion to introduce him. It took us a little aback when last year, at a dinner, Pollio calmly announced that he would him-

51

self read his own latest work. There is, I know, no real difference between reading your writings aloud to your friends and sending them copies to read, especially as most of us are likely to have them read to us by a slave or freedman. And yet, I and others were a trifle shocked. A faint suggestion was present of a Roman as an entertainer. It is hard to shake off our inherited prejudice against such things.

It all went off very well. Pollio read us a speech in the manner of Isocrates, much more pointed than most of those of Isocrates. It was really an attack on the modern oratorical style, that of Cicero principally, but not merely Cicero's. He professed, I think sincerely, a great admiration for Cicero as a man and as a philosopher, but he strongly opposed the influence of his style in oratory; he called it Asianic.

There were some who agreed with him in the excited discussion that followed, but, after all, not many. I think he is quite wrong. I see nothing Asianic, nothing florid, nothing turgid or overladen, in Cicero's speeches. Of course they are a little more elaborated than they were when delivered, but there is no substantial difference. I should say that Cicero was as little Asianic as Pollio is an Atticist, although he claims to belong to that movement.

There is hardly a dinner at Rome of any note at which the question of style has not come up, and the Asianists and the Atticists have belabored each other with great vigor. Pollio's speech gave a new impetus to it. Many of my young friends have been at some pains to show me how purely they atticize even in Latin, and have pared their sentences until one would think that an adjective were an affront to a noun. In a way they are right; it often is.

Marcus Varro has laughed with me more than once over the efforts they put themselves to, to write Latin as Lysias might have written Greek. Varro himself is curiously indifferent about his own style. When a man knows so much and writes so much, he can hardly trouble himself about art in literary expression. And yet Varro, if anyone, knows all the devices and tricks of Latin speech as he certainly knows more Latin words than any other living man. Grammarians—Varro calls himself one—are rarely good rhetoricians, but that is not an absolute rule. There were few men more honestly interested in grammar than Caesar the Dictator, and what a style the man had in his speeches! Pollio, who disliked him heartily, puts him at the head of his Atticists.

I have been somewhat taken to task by young Statilius, who has steeped himself in the study of our Teacher as no one else has, for what he calls my excessive occupation with the fripperies of style. And our solemn and dignified Lucius Torquatus was still more insistent. "Where is there," he asked, "in any line the Master wrote, or in anything that we know that comes from him, a single word about tropes and antitheses, or about closing rhythms or opening rhythms, or any nonsense of that sort? Our adversaries jeer at his style. I welcome their scoffing and glory in it." That was also Zeno's view when I heard him at Athens years ago. It was natural enough for a Sidonian like Zeno to speak contemptuously of Greek style. He never really learned to speak Greek. Torquatus, on the contrary, has a good ear and speaks Greek well.

Luckily, not all our Epicureans are so unyielding. My old Gallic friend, Titus Catius, was not like that. His translation of Epicurus is bald enough, but it was intentionally so. As far as he could, he rendered his text word for word. But he knew what a richer and more colorful writing might be, and he had a library as well and as carefully selected as the most fastidious taste could wish. They tell me his son is an authority on cook-

53

ery and is composing a treatise on fish. Each man to his tastes. I should myself rather eat well-prepared fish than read about the method of preparing it.

It cannot be denied that our Master did not enjoy books as much as some of us do. But it would be absurd to say that he despised them. He despised nothing but selfishness and cruelty and the kind of incontinence that involves yielding to every impulse without reflecting on its consequences. Granted that his ear was not as keen or as sharp as Plato's, in spite of the little tract he wrote on music. There is more mathematics in that treatise than any delight in harmonics. But it is not, after all, for the fineness of his hearing that we remember Plato, and exquisite periods alone would not have established the Academy. I know many a wandering musician whose feeling for sound is as good as Plato's.

Of course, the love of literature does not depend entirely on sounds. There is no good writing, I think, unless the sounds are lovely to hear. But that is not enough. There must be the suggestion of things beautiful to look at or satisfying to contemplate. And that too, I fear, meant less to our Master than it did to many lesser men, as far as imagery itself was concerned. His sensitiveness lay in another field. His companions tell us how his eyes would light up when he talked of the stars and their relation to one another and described the movement of the elements. And he was still more moved when he discussed with his disciples the obligations of friends to each other.

I have a somewhat more concrete mind. That was also true of Metrodorus, and yet he was the most beloved of the disciples. Phaedrus, whom I knew at Athens as well as Rome, was, just as in my case, less stirred by the beauty of a mathematical demonstration than by a line of Simonides.

How many of the actual hours of my life have been spent in

reading and being read to, I am sure I cannot count. I do not begrudge a single one of them, not even the hours spent in discovering that a book was not worth reading. That has happened very rarely. My library is quite as large as Pollio's. The books it contains are for the most part old books, that have at least the guaranty of the approval of many generations. There is not a scroll there of which one could say that the time spent in reading it was wasted.

So far as new books are concerned, except those of friends whose writings I cannot in courtesy refuse to read, every book I have bought or have had copied was acquired at the suggestion of some person of judgment. I can count on the taste of my freedmen, Dionysius, or Salvius, or Nicanor, as I could on Cicero himself, and to these four, or to Tiro, I owe most of the books I possess which were written by contemporaries.

There is, I say, much talk of style among us, even among the gentry who can barely read if they can read at all. I am told that one of my neighbors on the Quirinal, who seems quite legally to possess the name of Aulus Gabinius Serapio, and would be known for a beady-eyed Egyptian whatever name he bears— this fellow-citizen and neighbor of mine has become quite a literary connoisseur by proxy. He has bought a number of well-read slaves with strong memories who at a signal will quote for him at his dinners from Homer or Thucydides or Meleager or Callimachus, whenever a quotation seems necessary. He has not quite had the impertinence to invite me, but I am sure he will in a short time. Until that privilege is granted me, I can only speak of him as that inimitable Syrian, Publilius, describes him to us. Publilius is going to put Serapio on in a mime. I hope he will do it soon. My friends must not postpone the pleasures they intend for me too long.

Evidently there are many persons like Serapio who think

they can buy good taste as they can buy a good memory by the simple process of purchasing a slave who has one or both. Luckily, there are many men about me who have no need of buying either. I cannot remember even in the days when we were the privileged young members of the group that contained Marcus Antonius the elder, Lucius Crassus and the great lawyer, Quintus Mucius, so pleasant and exciting a stir all around of men who write because they love the art of writing quite as much as the things they write about. One can almost hear the buzzing of the bees that Plato spoke of in the *Io*. And the honey I have tasted so far has been sweet and strong.

Will the new world that is being made have a place for all this? I suppose so, whether it will be Marcus Antonius who manages it, or Caesar Octavian. Of course, it will be different in the former case. It seems likely enough that under Antonius the center of all activity will be Alexandria and not Rome and that the Jupiter of the Capitol will have to emigrate to the Nile and become a horned Ammon or a snouted Anubis. I care less, I am free to say, about what will happen to Jupiter than about what will happen to those clever and fascinating young persons whom Maecenas has gathered about him—to Vergilius and Varius and Horatius and Valgius and Gallus. They will wither fast enough, I fear. And the kind of combed and tended lapdog writers that Alexandria will furnish in the place of them will be little compensation. But this can really be no concern of mine, except vicariously; or better, in anticipation, since we feel what we feel, whether it is a memory or a prophecy.

When Pollio gave his first public reading the discussion became so warm and personal that I was glad when it was over. It so happened that Gaius Trebatius and Aulus Cascellius escorted me home. That was not an accident. These two lawyers are much my juniors, but we have a great deal in common—if nothing else, our attachment to Marcus Cicero. Trebatius was bitter against Pollio. There was no need, he thought, of inciting men to cavil at the style of the greatest of Roman orators. "The jackals," he said, "are only waiting for a chance to fling themselves on his literary fame, as they have long done on his political reputation. Pollio will only get the credit of truckling to Caesar by an attack on Caesar's victim."

I tried to calm him. "I don't believe that Pollio can be accused of any subservience. He has always been like that. He qualifies everything. You remember that he thought there were many dull passages in Homer. And style just now means more to him than anything else. Certainly more than politics."

Cascellius smiled and nodded. "And quite right," he said. "It is vastly more significant than politics, at least for us. Our rulers have taken political activity as their form of amusement and left questions of style to us. It is altogether proper for Gaius Asinius to initiate a frenzied discussion of the best style in oratory just at the moment when oratory ceases to have any purpose or function in the state."

We continued the discussion till late into the night. And for much of the next few days, for that matter, since they both remained with me as my guests. Cascellius did me the honor to say that there were not many houses in which he could speak as freely as he can in mine of his bitterness at the ruin of the Roman state. I think he is mistaken. Caesar Octavian is not much interested in the private and domestic outbursts of the Irreconcilables. As long as they do not actively oppose him, they may say what they like and leave unsaid what they choose. And, above all, they may say what they like, if they say it well. He has, himself, a part of his kinsman's interest in style.

But I suppose Cascellius is right. There was interest enough in oratorical style twenty years ago when any law-day in the

Forum or any political gathering might find Marcus Cicero stalking to the platform with his assured and confident stride, and when ten thousand persons, crowded into any corner that would hold a man, gave that little sigh of pleasurable satisfaction at the very first words which issued with such magnificent resonance from his lips. Whether or not his hearers were on his side when he began, they were fairly sure to be so when he ended.

The audience, it is true, never thought of his style. But Marcus did. He prepared with as much care as Quintus Roscius or Aesopus did when they studied their roles for the theater. And he loved arguing with me and his other friends on every point of rhetoric or literary effectiveness. His books on style in oratory would of themselves show that. But active as our interest then was, it has doubled and trebled in the past few years, although now we can scarcely count on hearing a Cicero or anybody else address a Forum packed with men on edge with expectancy.

Perhaps Cascellius overstates it, but in the main it cannot be denied that when an activity has lost its special reason for existence it may still furnish food for much discussion. What he disregards is the fact that contemplation is also an activity. I do not admit that it is a purposeless one.

VII

A LARGE PART of my library I have given over to Dionysius to use for copying. He has been in charge of that now for twenty-five years, as well as of disposing of the books I copy in order to sell. I have sold books on a fairly large scale, and on the whole it has not been unprofitable. Out of the profits Dionysius has bought a great many books for me, has seen to the repairs of my library, and has also provided all the living expenses for my copyists. These copyists are the only slaves I have at Rome that were not born on my own property or my uncle's, except the bearers and the watchmen.

Several times, Dionysius has assured me that I could make a great deal of money by hiring out my copyists. They are probably the best in Rome, and he is inordinately proud of them since most of them he himself selected and trained. Dionysius is a good fellow, but he simply refuses to understand that Romans do not regard it as proper to let out their slaves for profit. He says he sees no reason against it. It is commonly done, as I very well know, in Greek cities, even by men of wealth and standing.

As a matter of fact, there really is no reason against it. There rarely are satisfactory reasons for social customs, and often the reasons that once were satisfactory cease to be so later. Nor is this custom an absolute rule with us at Rome. My troupe of gladiators—I never set eyes on them—were bought for me by Athamas to be hired out. I can hardly see what else I could have done with them. Apparently it was an excellent troupe. At any rate they fought with considerable success and not without profit to me. And of the original fourteen there were twelve able-bodied survivors when I sold the entire troupe to Sextus Aufidius.

Cicero went to the Circus once at one of their contests, but I declined. I am a little squeamish about fights in the arena. It is not a spectacle I take pleasure in. Curiously enough, the Master encouraged his disciples to go to the games, and there is not much to choose in the way of bloodiness between the boxing matches in Greece and our gladiatorial combats. But then, he merely encouraged those to go who enjoyed going. I do not.

Only this morning, Dionysius came to me with a question that he has asked me some twenty times. "Titus Pomponius, what shall we do with this?" "This" is the book that Appius Claudius gave me before his death and which I half promised some day to copy and publish. That was sixteen years ago.

It is a sad piece of business. Appius' book on divination is silly enough, but this other book is crammed full of stuff about ghosts and vampires and witches and evocation of the dead. I have had it gone over a dozen times and have taken out some of the things that were supremely ridiculous, but it remains essentially what it was.

We have been the bankers for the Claudians now for three generations—for all the Claudians, the patrician Nerones and the plebeian Marcelli, although today there is little enough to

60

choose between these two families in nobility or distinction. But our association has been especially close with the most authentic Claudians of all, the family of Appius. It involved me in no little embarrassment at times, in the worst days of Publius Clodius' dominance, because of my intimacy with Marcus Cicero. But scamp as Publius was—and he was as nearly empty of any moral responsibility as a man could well be—he made it a special point not to break with me although he had no reason to doubt what I thought of him.

There were moments when I thought his brother Appius the more difficult of the two. He was hard and arrogant and overbearing and vain, for all that he remained respectable and a supporter of the state, but he was really fond of me and accepted admonition from me when he would have refused it from any other man. This was especially true toward the end of his life, when he was with me constantly and when he exacted the promise from me that I would revise his books and publish them, particularly this treatise of his on evocation of ghosts.

I see no escape from it. I am under no legal obligation, of course, but naturally this has nothing to do with the matter. Dionysius takes a malicious delight in bringing the book to my attention, and insists on quoting from it especially if one of those inveterate scoffers, Gallus or Horatius, is present. I can hear the derisive laughter of all my friends if there should be published under my direction and distributed by my freedman a book in which the story is told, as sober fact, how Appius' country steward's child was attacked at night by a screech owl which sucked a pint of blood from its neck, and how this screech owl was next day identified by a fragment of the child's swaddling clothes and turned out to be a malignant hag living in a hut not far from the steward's house. It is hard to believe

61

that grown men tell these stories except for amusement, and if we recall that Appius had the same education as all of us it becomes incredible.

This business of owls turned into hags, and hags into owls, of ghosts with curved talons perching by night on their enemies' breasts and tearing invisible but painful furrows in their faces, is weird and grotesque nonsense. Whenever it is mentioned among us, someone is sure to turn to Maecenas as an authority because his Etruscan ancestors certainly fitted their monuments with all sorts of red monsters, tusked and shaggy, half-human creatures, breathing forth flames and transfixing poor souls with tridents or pounding them with hammers.

Maecenas never fails to rise to the occasion, especially if he is a little flushed with wine. For every story told he has another, more elaborate and horrifying than the preceding one, and if poor Appius were still alive he would probably never have left any one of those dinners except shaking as though he had the ague and spitting right and left to avert the evil spirits.

That most of these stories were invented on the spot he would probably refuse to believe, just as an occasional visitor of mine, one of the new senators from the north, Quintus Licinius, evidently takes them all as authentic happenings. He sits visibly quaking while Maecenas spins out tale after tale. Licinius is a soldier almost without education, and, to do him justice, without pretense. But with a little common sense he might realize that the storyteller would scarcely tell these things with such evident delight if he believed them. One may well say that Maecenas is the least hag-ridden man of our acquaintance.

Among the people I meet frequently there are, of course, few men like Licinius and fewer still like Appius. But I am afraid that the state of mind from which Titus Lucretius piously declared our Master had freed the human race is still dominant

62

enough, even if it does not always express itself in visions of vampires and ghosts and tusked and tousled monsters of the Underworld. It is strange and absurd that Appius should believe in such things, or even Licinius, but we should not think it absurd if an Apulian peasant believed in them, or a gladiator or a sailor. The majority of my fellow Romans may or may not live in dread of vampires, but they have thousands of other gods and godlings, and I am not sure that the vampire that bled Appius' steward's infant child was very much more disgusting or cruel than the Zeus of so many dignified Greek accounts— the Zeus of Pollio's Antiope, to take an example quite vividly in my mind.

As far as the Greek stories are concerned, they are poetic tales, perhaps not to be taken more seriously than the imaginative and extemporized horrors with which Maecenas regales us so often. I know Greeks of all sorts very well. And I have met some quite stupid ones. But the Greeks who could write great tragedies and lyrics—surely they did not literally believe that Zeus had the manners and self-restraint of a Numidian brigand, for only a Numidian brigand could act toward persons weaker than he was as Zeus is said to have acted toward Antiope, toward Alcmena, Io, or Prometheus.

Evidently most of these stories were never meant to be believed. They could not have been so meant, because they changed from shrine to shrine and from tragedy to tragedy. I will do most of my contemporaries the justice to suppose that, whatever they believe about the gods, they do not believe either the priests or the poets.

But they do believe in gods who conceivably could act as the tragic or the comic Zeus acts, or as vampires and the Furies act, or the Fufluns and the Tuchulcha and the Sethlans whom Maecenas' ancestors pictured so hideously on the walls of their

63

tombs. I should not trust a god who had the power to torture my body or my soul, even if he loftily declared in thunder-tones that he did not intend to do so, no matter how angry he got. I prefer to think of the gods, as our Master understood them, as beings who by their nature and essential character could not possibly deport themselves like a goat in rut or like a wolf tearing a lamb.

I thought much about the gods when I was a boy, and a little more when I was a young man and was listening to my teachers at Rome and Athens and Rhodes and Ephesus. There were a great many of them, and they explained in many different ways, most of them in violent contradiction with each other, how the universe was made and governed, how its parts fitted into each other, and what man's role was in the vast world in which he moved. Hours of argument and reading and many more hours of contemplation in those bright and colorful years were spent on these high themes.

But since my early manhood I have thought less and less about the gods; and now, at the end of my life, shortly before I should be joining them if I were an adept of Eleusis or Samothrace or some other Society of Initiates, I think about them scarcely at all. They come into my mind chiefly when Dionysius brings me that unfortunate book that I have on my conscience, and with pretended solicitude warns me that if I do not publish it the imps and goblins it contains will flood the house. It is the fault of the poets and the peddlers of spells and charms that I cannot think of Appius' witches without being reminded of the gods.

Evidently there are gods. A rock is dead, and a lizard crawling on it is alive, and the difference is certainly that the one is moved by something within itself and the other is not, although it too can be torn away by outside forces to be hurled hundreds of yards further, and can work harm enough on what is in its way. If men call that something a spirit or a soul or a force or an efficient cause, it does not much matter. It is composed of atoms like everything else, and it moves because the atoms must move until by some scarcely thinkable accident they all at the same moment find themselves in such combinations that they are perfectly adjusted in every respect. When that happens, there will be no world. Or, perhaps, there will be nothing but gods in the world.

Until that happens, the subtle and fine disposition of atoms which makes a living thing out of dead bones and sinews will continue to take the thousand various forms that it does, and produce here men and there butterflies, trees, and oxen. And, I suppose, it can be said that in producing the rational human soul they have gone as far as they can within the compass of tangible and corruptible bodies. But who will prove to us that they cannot transcend this limit, and that they may not assume relations so fine and subtle that they need no bodily form to envelop them at all? This we may suppose is the case of the gods. Such beings cannot suffer or feel pain, cannot hunger or thirst, cannot love, if to love means to desire something that they do not possess. They can have no contact with us, nor we with them, for their movement is a harmonious movement, each of them complete within itself and incapable of disturbance or deflection. Nor are they within any of the worlds. If they were, they could be swept in the whirl of atoms that carry the countless bodies in each world on and on in resistless motion so that all things continually break and re-form, increase and lessen, grow and decay. No, the gods must live between the worlds, where there is no cold or heat, no weakness or death. If any of our senses could ever apprehend them at all, perhaps they would seem merely like beautiful music, too faint

65

and far off to tire us by repetition, too perfect and complete to rise to climaxes or die away in cadences.

We can imagine such beings, and imagining is a kind of knowing. And the fact that always and everywhere men have imagined gods, have felt directly—without the guidance of the wisest of Teachers—that what is crudely and imperfectly combined in their souls is finely and perfectly combined elsewhere— that fact is, I think, of value. The highest type of soul that a body can contain, the soul of man, is shown by this fact to be aware of its insufficiency, and that justifies our imagination in demanding a higher step in the process of combination.

Of course, we can imagine not only gods, but also griffins and chimaeras and centaurs and satyrs. I do not myself believe that there are such animals, but strangely shaped beasts are daily brought to us from India and Africa—beasts so strange that I shall not take it upon myself to say that an enterprising traveler might not bring from beyond the confines of the Red Sea an animal with the head of a goat, the beak of an eagle, and the tail of a snake. But whether there are griffins or not is not important. If there were such creatures, they would simply be additional examples of a kind we have already. No imagination of ours could have invented as many forms of living things as can be met with in any forest or on any mountainside, and there is no special need of stimulating our fancy to add to them.

It is different with the gods. They are not like us in any way, or like any other living thing. If we nonetheless imagine them, it is probably not an idle fantasy, but a real need of our reason. But there is no need of our reason which can impel us to imagine gods that are exactly like men and like a rather poor sort of man, gods that are angry, gods that beguile shepherdesses and shepherds for a single moment of gratification, gods that deceive and are deceived; or, for that matter, gods that sit in

66

resplendent and beautiful but very human bodies on thrones of ivory in houses of marble and fretted gold.

If there were such gods, I can only say that I have met men who were much better and nobler than the gods, and a few quite as beautiful, and if the adepts of Eleusis spend their lives in preparation in order to live forever with Demeter and Kore and Dionysius, I venture to declare that I should prefer to have lived a year in the Garden with Epicurus, and that I would not exchange for the deathless company of the Olympians my years of intimacy with that very ungodlike man, Marcus Cicero.

Plato would pour myrrh on the head of a poet, crown him with fillets of soft white wool, and escort him to some other city than the state he had fashioned in his mind. I should be glad to do so for the Olympian gods, if any one of them ventured to appear in bodily form, as our legends say they have so often appeared. But the poets who wrote of them I should retain, and I should even encourage them to invent more and more tales of these personages. Whatever one may say about the gods, and however sure we may be that they would be extremely bad citizens, it cannot be denied that they would be picturesque ones. The average god, I am inclined to think, would not differ very much from Publius Clodius.

When I was a boy on my father's estate in the Sabine Hills, I accompanied the flocks to the fields with the shepherds and with old Eutychus, my tutor. I remember very clearly the stories told by one of the shepherds, a Thracian whose name I never knew. He was called merely "The Thracian." It was the first suggestion I had that there were different gods in Thrace from the gods to whom I poured out libations or on whose altars I dropped cakes of spelt and honey. The Thracian told about Zalmoxis and how every five years a messenger was sent to him. They threw a man selected by lot into the air and caught him on the point of their spears. His soul, it was assumed, carried the message to Zalmoxis. And the Thracian told also how they shot arrows into the sky whenever it thundered, to prevent the bolt from injuring them. Their thunder god is not Jupiter and they think they can frighten him.

If I had been an Epicurean at seven or eight years of age and if Titus Lucretius had already written his beautiful book, I should doubtless have murmured, *Tantum religio potuit suadere malorum.* But I fear that at that time I was both horrified and fascinated, and although I was glad we sent no messages to Zalmoxis, I never doubted that out there in Thrace he lived and ruled.

The Thracian said he had often seen gods and that once, in his native country, he had encountered a satyr—a real goat-satyr with the hind quarters and hoofs of a goat and the body of a man. I have no doubt he thought he was telling the truth. Lucius Sulla had a satyr brought to him on one of his expeditions in Greece. The creature was released and ran off into the woods making bleating or whinnying sounds. It is true that Sulla sometimes said he himself saw it and sometimes that one of his officers saw it. And sometimes he admitted that it was in the early morning after a long night's carouse and that he did not notice how satyr-like the creature looked till it ran off.

But my Thracian had no doubt about the gods he had seen. And I believed him without question. Very often I sat on the hillside under a tree; and if the air was still and bright and the sky deep blue, so blue that it looked black, and no one was about except a few straggling sheep, I listened for the sound of pattering hoofs that would be different from the running of goats and hoped that in a flash of red and gold the Twins would suddenly be seen watering their snow-white horses at the spring near the maple grove, as I had seen them in my fancy a thousand times.

I saw and heard nothing that anyone might not have seen or heard. But I continually thought and wondered about the gods. I knew many names of gods, all the Homeric gods in their Greek names as well as their Latin names, and those hundreds of other named gods whom the poets after Homer invented and wrote about; but it is curious how my imagination played not so much with these as with those other gods of my ancestors who had no name, who were known only by what they did or even by the mere fact that they existed, no one knew how.

Indeed, very near the maple grove further up the hillside there was a rude little altar dedicated in the letters and spelling of a hundred years ago, to whatever was there "whether it is a god or a goddess." My father smiled when he passed it, and so did Eutychus, but my Thracian and I did not smile. I put garlands on it at every feast day and dropped my honeycake in front of it. The blackbirds got the honeycake, although they often had to fight the squirrels and magpies for it, but the shapeless and nameless and sexless god who lived there got my message, even if it did not involve throwing a man into the air and impaling him as he fell.

Time and time again I wondered what it would look like if it should appear, and what it would say if it spoke. Of course these fancies always took a human form, although the lower part of the body generally disappeared in a cloudy confusion of toga, but somehow I made him masculine and spoke of him as "he." I never managed to get an outline of his features. I told myself stories about him, gave him parents just as the other gods had. I wondered whether he was a sort of divine waif that had been exposed and abandoned in infancy, as girl babies are

69

exposed in the East and occasionally in Italy. Once Eutychus found me in tears about the poor desolate god that had never managed to get a temple, not the smallest or meanest, or even a cave or a grove, but merely had a little space on a sunny hill-side.

"Perhaps he is really a great god," I told my Thracian, "and is hiding there to see whether we shall honor him."

"No," he said, shaking his head. "He's not a great god. He doesn't appear because he isn't strong enough to manifest himself. He can't hurt us or help us. He can just barely tell us that he's there."

So we worshiped this vague and pitiful god with complete disinterestedness. At any rate the Thracian did. I must confess that the stories in which apparent beggars suddenly revealed themselves as gods in order to reward their benefactors played a part with me. But, after all, I did not really expect anything definite from this poor little god.

I have not visited my Sabine villa in many years. My freedman, Quintus, tells me the altar is still there and that the farm slaves have enclosed it with a rectangle, inaugurated and consecrated with all due ceremony. My Thracian is long dead, but some of the older slaves remember him and recall what he said about my worship at the altar. They treat the new shrine with great awe. Not merely rustic garlands or an occasional cake, but a due ritual with the sacrifice of a kid, is performed there on my birthday.

They will have it that such position as I have attained, particularly my wealth and my long life, are due to the protection of this god. Above all, they think it is he who has saved my life from the many perils that beset it, and that he continues to watch over me and them.

Well, I shall soon be beyond his protection, but I do not re-

70

pudiate it. Gaius Caesar was the darling of the gods, the great gods, who could not save him from his murderers. Now he has become a great god himself. Against them all I will match my shy little patron, "whether it is a god or a goddess." Even our Master would have no objection to continuing to give him the slight honors that have now become a custom after nearly seventy years.

I have committed the god to the care of my freedman Quintus and his descendants.

VIII

LAST WEEK WAS the week of Parentalia, our season of doing honor to the dead. Agrippa has not yet returned, but the rest of us went to the Caecilian sanctuary on the Appian Way, I and Atticula and Quintus and Dionysius and Athamas and Alexis, together with my cousin Marcus Pomponius and my other cousin, Lucius Caecilius. We bore the gifts of water and wine, milk and honey and oil in little jugs and set them before Pillia's altar that stood in front of the urn in which her ashes are kept. On the altar itself, Atticula put garlands of bright flowers. Then, with the proper rites, Quintus killed the sacrificial black pig and poured its blood on the earth. When the sacrifice was over, Atticula, clinging close to me, faltered out the ceremonial greeting, *"Salve, sancta parens,"* and Alexis offered each of us a cake of spelt, and placed another on the ground next to the offering.

It is a solemn ceremony, but not really a sad one. I have taught Atticula to understand that performing it is a duty we owe the state, and that it is better to conform to harmless customs than to arouse suspicion and dislike among our neighbors and fellow-citizens, to whom these things are holy and important. Except as an ancestral tradition, we know that such rites are meaning-less, since there is no Pillia any longer, any more than there is last year's snow still on the hills. It is not the ceremony itself but the memory it evokes, which moves us so profoundly year after year, and makes Atticula weep in my arms, when we rise to take our departure.

At the Charistia, at my house, on the following day, all our kinsmen met as usual. Marcus Cicero came, too, and Tiro with him. It was the first Charistia at which my baby granddaughter —Agrippina, they have decided to call her instead of Vipsania— could be presented to her relatives, and with Atticula and her baby, there came also the child's betrothed husband, Tiberius Nero, escorted by his uncle, Marcus Drusus. The ceremonies were simple and the occasion was pleasant, if a little too sober. We have luckily had no family feuds to smooth over for a long time; no hostile brothers or cousins to reconcile. It was differ-ent in the old days during the lifetime of my sister, when every year presented a new problem. She and her husband, Quintus Cicero, were a thoroughly ill-assorted couple.

Tiberius was very attentive. He inquired solicitously after my health, and at once began speaking in Greek of his new tutor, Theodorus, with whom he is studying the poets. He speaks very well indeed. His associates believe that he is proud and super-cilious. I should think it would be truer to call him especially reserved in public. He can be garrulous when we are alone to-gether, although he rarely smiles. It is a rather difficult position in which he finds himself, and young as he is, he is acutely sen-sible of it. It will be better when he goes to Athens with Theo-dorus. Both Caesar and his mother direct him a trifle too much.

He left a little before the rest, and made his excuses to Attic-ula and me with ceremony but without constraint. Indeed, he playfully bowed to his affianced bride and stretched out his hand

73

to her. She seized his thumb and held it tight in her soft fingers. All the women present cried out that it was a good omen.

Agrippina is quite a little darling and, it seems to me, resembles Pillia. I am afraid she has much of the delicacy of Pillia's constitution. I can only hope for Tiberius that she will have something of her spirit.

Pillia was young when we were married, not quite twenty, and I was more than forty. I had resisted all the urging of my friends to marry for so long that most persons assumed I intended to die a bachelor in defiance of our traditions. It was Marcus Cato who persuaded me finally. The Stoics agree with us in this thing, that all the duties that one owes to the state should be performed in so far as they do not contradict or render difficult the way of life we have chosen. And if these duties are sanctioned by ancient custom and by the particular character of our state, they come to us with a double force.

I hesitated for a long while. I felt flattered when Lucullus suggested his grand-niece Licinia to me, the daughter of his nephew Gnaeus, and when Servius Sulpicius offered me his daughter. If I declined the honor, it was because I feared that such a marriage would involve me in a career which I had deliberately rejected and for which I was not fitted.

I first saw Pillia at the house of her father, Quintus Celer, at a dinner to which he had invited Gaius Caesar and Cicero and me. Celer was an active Caesarian of no special standing with his chief, but of varied and appreciated usefulness. Caesar wished me to give him letters of introduction to my correspondents in Alexandria and Antioch where Celer was being sent on a special mission. This was long before Caesar's dictatorship. Indeed it was before Marcus was consul, and at a time when Marcus himself was taken generally to be one of the great supporters of the popular party.

74

Pillia withdrew early. I heard her speak only once. Her voice was like the vibration of a lute string. It is more than thirty-five years ago, but I shall never forget it, as I heard it then. I looked after her when she walked toward the peristyle and caught sight of her face in profile as she turned, her slender figure swaying slightly and her dark hair catching the moving light of the lamps.

Evidently no one noticed that she had impressed me so profoundly. Celer was genuinely surprised when a month later I asked him to give her to me as my wife, if she consented. He agreed effusively. The formal betrothal took place the next day, and she was taken to my house during the following week, with a minimum of ceremony and festivity, and, I am afraid, with a minimum of approval of my friends, especially Marcus Cicero.

Marcus disliked Celer, even when they supported the same political doctrine. He thought him subservient and petty, in spite of his energy and zeal and his considerable power of oratory. I shared Cicero's judgment of him and my relations with my father-in-law, while cordial and friendly, as was proper, were never intimate. It was natural that Cicero's dislike should increase, as it did, when he became definitely one of our party, and Celer remained an eager and whole-hearted adherent, first of the Coalition, and finally of Caesar. Marcus was barely civil to him when he met him at my house.

But he grew fond of Pillia as she did of him. It was difficult not to be fond of Pillia, and equally, I think, difficult not to grow fond of Marcus, perhaps because of those very extremes of exaltation and depression of which Servius Sulpicius disapproved so intensely. He poured himself out with abandon in every phase of his emotion, whenever he felt sure he was among friends, and he was always sure of that with us.

Pillia used to say that it was like being on a hilltop with a great wind blowing through the trees to hear him, and as Atticula grew up, she and her mother would watch him with obvious fascination, whenever he spoke. I have seen the two, silently gazing at Marcus, who paced the floor, denouncing, upbraiding, explaining, despairing, protesting and exultantly triumphing. Their lips were parted and their eyes sparkled. They knew him well enough to laugh a little at his intensity without offending him. Above all, we did not interrupt him. We were good listeners, all three of us. Marcus needed listeners, and we needed him to listen to.

He had little of that in his own house. Terentia was always querulous, even in their best years, long before the breach between them. And Tullia married very early.

He grew very fond, I say, of Pillia. When Publius Clodius procured his banishment, she was heart-broken. She never forgave Publius and refused to see him from that time on. When her health began to fail in the year of Caesar's death, Cicero in spite of his absorption in his struggle with Marcus Antonius was overwhelmed with anxiety. He insisted on turning over his villa at Cumae to her, because the doctors thought the Campanian sea air would improve her. I was in Athens and Cicero escorted her south himself, despite the critical situation in Rome and despite the fact that my freedman, Quintus, would of course have taken her there.

Cicero made it a special point to visit her at Cumae a few months later, when he went down for the funeral of Cornelia, the mother of Gnaeus Lucullus, whose daughter I once was to have married. He wrote to me enthusiastically of Pillia's condition.

Unfortunately, his optimism was unjustified. Cumae did Pillia no good. She grew steadily worse. When I brought her home in December, she had a slight paralytic stroke on the left side and although she recovered the use of her hand and foot, her condition grew slowly desperate.

It is now five years since she died. Prepared as we were, it was a catastrophe from which I have not yet recovered. Only with a great effort can I make myself dictate these words even now. The agony of recalling her death is the bitterest memory I have.

We lived together thirty years. I do not remember that in all that time she ever did anything or said anything that offended me. I do not remember a single moment in which her presence was burdensome to me. I never heard her speak without hearing some echoes of the voice that captivated me at that meeting so many years ago. She said nothing then, except what the most formal politeness required. "It is very kind of you, Titus Pomponius, to visit my father's house on such short notice, you who are so much occupied." It would not have seemed more beautiful if she had chanted a complete ode of Alcaeus.

I never gave her a rival. And I never loved any woman as I loved her. The slaves and freedwomen who had been my concubines before my marriage, I had in every instance dowered and married off. They and their husbands are established in various places in Italy and Greece. Of the children they bore me, only two survived and both I emancipated early. One is living in Epirus as the manager of my estates there. The other is my freedman, Quintus, who has been to me all that a son could be.

His mother was a Rhodian woman of beauty and education. Her name was Nicandra. She died when Quintus was two years old. He was twelve years old when I married Pillia and they became devoted to each other almost at once. When Atticula

77

was born, Quintus took care of his sister as though he were her nurse. He taught her her letters and later took on himself the responsibility for her Greek education.

Atticula was our youngest. Our first two children died in infancy. She is exactly like her mother except that she is taller and, I am glad to say, much more robust. She resembles her especially in her voice and her gaiety. Not only Quintus and I idolized her, but Marcus Cicero also did. He showered an affection on her from her earliest childhood to which she fully responded. He wrote a number of letters to her, one when she was six. She will not let Tiro and me publish any of them with the rest of Cicero's correspondence. They are far too precious, she says, to be peered at by vulgar eyes. Pillia also would not let us publish the letters she received.

Pillia's own education was limited, a little more so than should have been the case in the daughter of a good family. She lost her mother early and her father was too busy with politics to concern himself much with her. As a matter of fact, she had less aptitude for letters than Atticula and less interest in them. Indeed, she was not clever, not as clever as Sempronia and Servilia and Clodia, but I do not think any reasonable person who knew her would doubt her vast superiority in every other respect to those distinguished ladies.

There are many men in Rome who speak of our present attitude toward women as a sad case of degeneracy. Our grandmothers were illiterate, and were rarely seen in public. They were subject to regulation in what they wore. They could be divorced for drinking wine. And still, we are told, they were the supreme exemplars of what women should be.

I have sometimes wondered. Within the sanctuary of the Claudians on the Appian Way, there is the grave of a lady of their family who must have died, I suppose, more than a hundred years ago. Appius told me that he thought she was the daughter of a Gaius Pulcher who was praetor about that time, a kinsman but not an ancestor of his. The tombstone bears an inscription that I have often read.

Beneath her name and her husband's, and the statement of her age, there are eight verses. The trimeters are a little heavy, but not more so than in the dramatic poems of the same time. I have read the lines so often that I remember them.

One little moment, stranger! Brief the tale I tell.
Hid in this hideous tomb a lovely lady lies.
Claudians her parents were; Claudia, her name as well.
She dearly loved her husband, nor in any wise
Had left him, but by death. Only two sons had she.
One walks the earth and one beneath the earth doth lie.
Pleasant her speech. She bore herself most gracefully.
Her house she ordered and her wool she spun. Good-bye.

HOSPES · QVOD · DEICO · PAVLLVM · EST · ASTA ·
   AC · PELLEGE
HEIC EST · SEPVLCRVM · HAV · PVLCRVM · PVLCRAI
   · FEMINAE
NOMEN · PARENTES · NOMINARVNT · CLAVDIAM
SVOM · MAREITVM · CORDE · DILEXIT · SOVO
GNATOS · DVOS · CREAVIT · HORVNC · ALTERVM
IN · TERRA · LINQVIT · ALIVM · SVB · TERRA ·
   LOCAT
SERMONE · LEPIDO · TVM · AVTEM · INCESSV ·
   COMMODO
DOMVM · SERVAVIT · LANAM · FECIT · DIXI · ABEI

I had noticed the inscription long before, but I looked at it with special care at Pillia's funeral. The tomb is near the edge of the road. I stopped the litter when we returned and read the lines through completely, for the first time. Several of us remarked that except for one or two details they might have served as a eulogy of Pillia.

That is what our ancestors asked of their wives, beauty, grace of body, graciousness of speech, a male child, devotion to their husbands. And an absorption in their household tasks. "Her house she ordered and her wool she spun." It doubtless had its special charm, the house of Claudia, whose husband, it is clear, loved her well and missed her sorely. Pillia spun no wool. Whether she could or not, I never knew, but she had several slaves any one of whom could spin far better than she could possibly have done, because they had been trained to do it all their lives. It would have been unreasonable for her to do laboriously and only tolerably well what these could do easily and expertly—unless she had liked doing it. She managed our household because she did like doing it, although if she had chosen, she might have been relieved of that as well.

When she decided to learn to sing to the lute, and I invited the Ephesian Chaerestratus to teach her, there was, I know, more than one murmur of disapprobation. Her father even professed himself shocked, but he promptly withdrew his objection when I assured him that I saw no harm in it.

There certainly is no harm in it, in spite of the fact that our ancient Lucretias and Valerias apparently thought it unbecoming for a Roman matron to furnish entertainment or amusement even to her own family. What our heroines forgot was that they might desire to amuse and entertain themselves. Singing has long been a proper thing to teach women, and if they may be taught to sing, there is not much sense in refusing to let them be well taught, provided they have the aptitude for it. I suppose the scandal of Sempronia has seemed to justify the supporters of the older method. Of that lady it was said that she had every female accomplishment and no female virtue. And it is quite true that there was no professional Milesian dancer or musician who had greater skill in these arts than she, and few men who were better read or wittier.

No doubt there are such things as female accomplishments, things that women can do better than men. But we are taught that there is no sex in virtue. And if Sempronia was dissipated and coarse in her way of living, that was no greater vice in her than the same qualities created in Marcus Caelius. I had no fear that learning music from the greatest living musician would turn Pillia into a Sempronia.

That she went out rarely was her own choice. Some of our ladies go frequently to the Circus. Atticula went a few times, once escorted by Marcus himself. But Pillia was not fond of crowds and disliked the thought of bloody combats much more even that I did. Nor did she pay many visits, except the visits of deference and courtesy, which were numerous enough. Indeed, I have always thought that there was one respect in which we differed widely. She neither made many friends nor felt the need of them.

Philodemus wrote me eight exquisite Greek distichs to inscribe on her altar. I decided not to use them. Her urn has nothing but her name. "Pillia, daughter of Quintus Celer, wife of Quintus Caecilius." I do not insist that the passing stranger shall stop to hear of her. Those who were no strangers will not need an admonition to remember her.

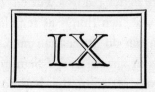

IX

I FELT A little weak this morning. Quintus says I fainted as I stepped out of my bed-room. It wasn't really a faint, but I was glad to be able to recline on my couch in the atrium. I forbade him to send for Atticula. Or for a doctor. A little later in the afternoon, I felt much better, and talked for several hours with Nepos who has been my guest the last five days.

It gave Quintus an excellent chance to deny me to other visitors, especially to those who have been a decided nuisance recently. There has been no such coming and going in my house for years.

Three days ago Saras arrived post-haste from Alexandria. He came at dusk so that, as he said, his visit would excite little comment. It was quite unnecessary. I have no objection to anyone knowing that I received him. It merely proves that I am still in communication with Antonius, and that is common knowledge.

Saras brought disturbing news. Marcus Antonius has quite made up his mind to a formal divorce from Octavia. The Egyptian, it seems, is becoming impatient. It was not so much the fact itself as its imminence that is disturbing. And evidently the personal breach between Caesar and Antonius, which will then become open and irreparable, would not of itself be disastrous. If it were not this one, some other fire-brand would start the conflagration.

In other respects, Saras brought me little that was new. Antonius sent me the most flattering greetings. He is much concerned about the reports of my illness. Egyptian physicians, it is well known, are the best in the world. One of the most famous was Tanuphris, his own and the Queen's personal attendant, a man of extraordinary skill. Saras had him in his train and Antonius begged me to consult him and to take his advice.

I told Saras I should do nothing of the kind. I am fully aware of my condition and have decided on the proper remedy. I am in no mood for amulets and incantations. Saras assured me that Tanuphris uses quite different methods. But I declined to listen. Whatever his methods are, I cannot see how they can profit me.

And, of course, it was not merely to bring me this physician that Saras slipped into my house with such a parade of secrecy. Antonius had another message for me, or rather messages. Saras insisted on seeing me absolutely alone and even then all his communications were in whispers.

Did Agrippa know how extremely high an opinion of him Antonius held?

"Why not ask Agrippa?" I suggested. "He is at Misenum, inspecting the ships."

Saras grinned at me. The picture of Cleopatra's emissary actually getting a private interview with Agrippa in full view of the fleet at Misenum was, I admit, somewhat amusing.

"Will you give him the message?"

"Merely the message that Antonius thinks well of him? Certainly."

Saras grinned again. "Also," he murmured, "this further message. Antonius is very likely to sail for Hierapytna in Crete this month. If by any chance..."

"If Agrippa sails to Hierapytna this month," I said, "It will be entirely by chance."

Saras nodded. "I wonder," he said slowly, after a considerable pause, "If you have in mind that there might well be a marked change of affairs—a change, which might possibly make your condition a little insecure."

I had my answer ready. "No," I said, "I cannot imagine such a change of affairs."

Saras laughed. "You are probably right. It is absurd to speak to Atticus of insecurity. If a revolution takes place, it will merely be a new item in your collection."

He did not quite understand me, nor will Antonius when Saras reports my words. But, as a matter of fact, if the issue should be in favor of Antonius and I should still, by some un-foreseen accident, be alive, there are many things that I should dread more than what might happen to me.

Saras was not the only visitor of his kind. There have been no fewer than seven persons who in less than a week have sought urgent and very private interviews on matters of state. Why anyone should suppose that I would interfere, just before my dissolution, in things I have carefully avoided all my life, I cannot imagine. The atmosphere of intrigue, of bargaining, of proposing and counter-proposing would have been quite dis-tasteful if it had not been a little ludicrous. It was as if a dozen little moths had suddenly begun to fly about madly, not quite at a flame, but in search of one.

Probably the most picturesque of my visitors was a Greek-speaking Nabataean who bore the name of Lysanias. He was dressed in the desert fashion and the slaves who attended him had the darkest skins I have seen for a long while. It took some time to discover what his real object was. At first, he professed merely a desire to see my jewel cabinet, since he, or rather his employer, was himself a collector. It was soon clear that this was a pretext, but it was a good hour before I elicited the admission that he was sent directly by King Malchus and that this ally of Marcus Antonius was open to offers.

Malchus hates—and with good reason—both Cleopatra and his neighbor, Herodes of Judaea. He has, however, this in common with Herodes: both of them have been compelled to surrender territory to Cleopatra. But unlike Herodes he has not gained the confidence of Antonius and there seems little doubt that on one pretext or another he will find his entire realm of sand and rock turned over to some one of the Egyptian's bastards or flatterers or slaves.

Herodes, I think, is a man of real ability. Agrippa tells me he is the best soldier of all that swarming mass of Syrian tetrarchs and dynasts who keep the eastern limits of the Roman range of control in a state of constant ferment. The Greek agent of Herodes, Nicolaus of Damascus, was once brought to me by Philodemus. Nicolaus presented a letter from Herodes and a beautifully carved gold cup. I accepted it and sent him an embossed Corinthian sword in return. It was our only communication, but I have heard from him indirectly several times.

To do him justice, he has never offered to sell his power or his army. I think he is honestly attached to Rome, but like his rivals and associates, and everybody else, he is in some doubt as to who it is who will embody Rome in the years that are before us.

Nicolaus tells me that except for his ungovernable temper, something could be made of Herodes. He has a difficult people to rule over, all the more difficult because the sympathies of the great mass of them are with Parthia, and are violently anti-

85

Greek. But the nobility are Greek in speech and feeling and the Jews outside of Judaea, especially in Egypt and Asia, are also Greek. There are a number in Rome. Varro is very much interested in some of their speculations about the gods and thinks their conception of them is more like that of our ancestors. It may be so. Their god—Varro says they worship only one—is formless and invisible. Gnaeus Pompeius who entered their ancient shrine in Jerusalem, says there was nothing whatever in the adyton, except some carved stones and sacred utensils.

But apparently their god acts like a man, so it does not make very much difference what he looks like. I have been in Jerusalem and seen the shrine. It is small and dilapidated, but it is held in the greatest awe by most of the people in the East. It was somewhat stupid and unnecessary for Pompeius to insist on entering the adyton. He did it to show that he was not afraid of being killed. Their legends say that any one except their chief priest who entered, would be struck at once by a thunderbolt.

Pompeius was not killed. But that did not in the least decrease the faith of the people in the power of their god. Such things never do. Reason has nothing to do with the matter. If men applied reason to their ideas about gods, they would understand that the gods could not kill or brandish thunderbolts any more than they could beget human progeny or be pierced by human swords.

So, what with Saras and Lysanias and an emissary of Amyntas of Galatia and one from Archelaus of Cappadocia, and three more, from Crete and Olynthus and Pydna, there has been more political discussion in my house than I have heard since Cicero's death. The character of what was said has not made me regret the aloofness from these matters which has been the rule of my life.

86

It became the rule of my life a long while ago. I suppose one of the most beautiful books ever written is Plato's book on the state. I know it almost by heart. And one of the clumsiest of books is that of Zeno the Stoic on the state. But I have read that, too, with a great deal of interest, as well as almost every other discussion of the best form of human society. Neither of Cicero's two treatises on the subject is very well done, although both contain some fine things.

I have been stirred and moved by much of what I have read, but stirred and moved more than helped. Those who write about the state write best, as Plato did, when they write about a state that never was and which no man supposes ever could be. When they write as Cicero did, while they are themselves engaged in state affairs, their books are the poorer for it. I must admit, however, that one of the worst of books, so far as literary composition is concerned, that of Zeno, is also about a state that did not and could not exist.

This was one of the sharpest of the issues that we had with Marcus Cato. The Stoic state, he said, had this great advantage over all others. The state which Plato or Aristotle imagined needed a tyrant to establish, even if it contemplated no tyrant to govern it. It supposed an elaborate revolution. Existing forms must be abolished, new institutions created. It entailed war, the extermination or exile of those who would not submit. It required a constant and careful supervision to see that each person performed his proper function within it.

And if it were assumed that this could not be done at a single moment, the Platonic state was even harder to carry into effect. The slow flowering of the idea needed generations of single-minded and enlightened men training their fellow-citizens to create by slow steps the perfect type of state.

But the Stoic state was not like this at all. It needed no preparation, no ruthless clearing of the ground, no firm and purposeful arrangement of men in new classifications, no slow process of training or habituation. It did not even need, as all other forms of the state needed, a substantial number of citizens who would adopt and effectuate the form. One man alone could constitute the state.

I remember Lucius Crassus' lifted eyebrow and his mocking lips when Quintus Mucius expounded all this a little less than sixty years ago, while young Gaius Marius and Lucius Torquatus and I sat quietly behind the older men in the garden of Crassus' villa on the Liris, in view of the Arpinate hills.

"A city with one citizen, Quintus Mucius," he said, "has certain obvious advantages. It needs no censor."

Everybody laughed but Mucius. We youngsters, of course, did not join in. Crassus was censor in that year and was having a great deal of trouble. He had closed the Latin rhetorical schools because he declared that the teachers were frauds; and there had been violent protests.

Quintus Mucius, I said, did not laugh. "That is your great error, Lucius Licinius. It needs the severest censor. No man can be a citizen of the cosmopolis, until he has passed a muster which makes our determination of fitness seem, as it is, an unreal school exercise."

And that of course was Marcus Cato's position, much more fully thought out and vigorously presented than had been the case with Mucius, since Mucius, keen and sharp in mind and lofty in spirit as he was, had not quite the profound grasp of Cato. The Stoic cosmopolis was not a future ideal for which one slowly prepared. Nor yet a new organization of society which an autocratic ruler could put into effect by giving orders. It was present here and now and everywhere. It needed only one little resolution, and the walls and citadels of Rome or Athens or

Alexandria would melt into thin smoke and the Stoic could move about in a community, if there were other Stoics—or alone, if that were necessary—perfectly self-contained, with the tranquil consciousness that the state to which he belonged knew no injustice or wrong or suffering or imperfection.

It did not even require the abolition in imagination of the physical city of stone and brick and wood and earth. The Stoic did not deny the existence of these things, as the Gymnosophists did, of whom Pyrrho tells us. The stones were there, but they were indifferent. Within the physical city, the Stoic played the games that the others played, until he chose to quit or until the rules of the game or the tone of the activity demanded of him what the laws of his real city forbade. Nothing could happen to him for refusing to continue the game—except death. And death was nothing.

It is not an impossible notion. Cato, I think, realized it, and to a lesser extent, Servius Rufus, and Gaius Sextius, not to mention Posidonius who lived with me for several months when he visited Rome. In spite of the Stoic doctrine that there are no degrees in wisdom or virtue—you have it or you haven't it—these four Stoics were to a lesser or a greater extent citizens of the Stoic cosmopolis and some of them performed the functions of that citizenship more completely than the others.

They all had to some degree the power of shaking off the citizenship into which they were born and living, if only for a while, in that of the cosmopolis, self-contained, as Cato called it, and self-mastered, out of the reach of wrong or suffering or injustice.

But also, I think, out of the reach of happiness. A state which could conceivably consist of a single person is not one of which an Epicurean could be a member at all. For us, the highest happiness is that which comes from human association.

89

Indeed, except on the terms of some human association, there is no happiness whatever, not even in the real and substantial, but simple and somewhat perilous, pleasures of eating and drinking.

The state, like the clothes we wear, is devised for human happiness. Even more so than the clothes we wear. These may serve to adorn us and to please the eye but their primary purpose is to keep out the cold and in warm weather to keep us clean. They are to that extent a necessity. But to protect us from dangers we need no more organization than that of a wolf-pack. We do not need a state. Indeed, it almost seems as though for sheer protection, the wolf-pack is the better form. There is no type of the state that is ideally perfect, in spite of Plato. Time and place and the character of men determine what form will give us the greatest opportunity for happiness, and at any given moment, there may be several forms of the state in which such opportunity is present.

That was not the way I spoke and thought when I was twenty and when I and Marius and Torquatus and Marcus Cicero spent a summer together in the house of Cicero's father at Arpinum. Marcus was somewhat younger than we were, but his superior talents were already evident. At that time our idol was the elder Marius, the conqueror of Jugurtha, of the Cimbri, of the Teutones, six times a consul, the champion of the democracy. We were democrats, all of us. And in the books we read we knew no more resplendent figures than Cleisthenes and Pericles.

This was true in spite of the fact that in the house of Lucius Crassus, in that of the elder Marcus Antonius or of Quintus Mucius, we shared in an association with men vastly more cultivated and finely developed than the elder Marius, and we knew that all these men were oligarchs, strong opponents of

Marius and his party. We admired them unqualifiedly, as we admired Socrates and Plato, who also were the enemies of our doctrine. We were quite convinced that their political views were merely inherited. They had not yet accustomed themselves to the new impulse begun—or revivified—by Gaius Gracchus, whom young Marius and Torquatus and Cicero vowed to avenge as soon as they had the power to do so.

It was, doubtless, a premonition of my later beliefs that even then, when I was scarcely more than a boy, this talk of vengeance seemed to me childish. But otherwise I had no doubt that the domination of the Senate was an evil, and that the tribal assembly must be restored to its former power. Like my comrades, I loved the Roman state as I imagined it once had been and as I hoped it could once more be made to be.

Can one love an abstraction like the state, even as definite a one as the ancient Roman state? I think we managed to do so. And our love was no less when we became aware that our state had never really existed, that Rome had been an oligarchy when it expelled the Tarquins, when it put Pyrrhus to flight and, after a titanic struggle, overcome Hannibal, the greatest soldier that ever lived, according to Gaius Caesar and to Agrippa. We could at least fancy that it was an oligarchy in which the rulers used their power for the welfare of those they ruled. The oligarchy against which Gaius Gracchus and Marcus Drusus and Gaius Marius fought could hardly boast of such a purpose.

That is all very well. And as a matter of fact, I have never recaptured the ardor and glow that was in those days the mark of our political discussions. It is something in favor of a political theory that it can be ardent, especially if it is a generous and magnanimous ardor, an ardor in behalf of other persons. Those who share my present views, oligarchs, aristocrats, *optimates,* or

whatever we wish to call ourselves, are fervent enough sometimes but there is a little qualification to be made. We are quite
sure that ours is the best doctrine, but we are also quite sure that
our theory of government by the best men of the community
will mean that we are among the governors. It would carry a
little more conviction if what we advocated did not conduce so
much to our own advantage; if at some time there were a fervent adherent of aristocracy who did not classify himself among
the aristocrats.

I dare not place myself among the disinterested supporters of
aristocracy, because I think I may say with reason that I might,
as far as my personal choice was concerned, have taken a place
among the rulers of Rome, and that those who regarded themselves as undoubted aristocrats would have welcomed my participation. But if my theory of government has changed since the
days of those youthful conversations in Arpinum, it was not because I began to think more of my position and my importance,
but because I had come to the conclusion that there could be
no real democracy in the society that we know.

"*Isonomia,* the most beautiful of words," says the Persian
Otanes in Herodotus' story. Certainly it is a lofty conception of
society that no member is legally privileged beyond another,
that no one may be compelled to rank himself below another,
except in so far as he voluntarily recognizes a man as his superior. It does not mean that all men are of the same quality,
but it does mean that no man may claim by force a deference
his qualities and capacities do not of themselves inspire. My
Athenians in the old days professed to have established a real
equality. Most public offices, with the honors they implied and
the powers they carried with them, were held in turn by all
citizens and the order was determined by lot. The curious thing
was that this system in spite of Plato's and Xenophon's raillery,

92

did not work badly, no worse, surely, than any other method of selecting officers.

What makes democracy hopeless is that it ought to include the slaves; which would mean that there would be no slaves. It is impossible for life to be managed without slaves. The Stoics, to do them no less than justice, have imagined it, and to do them no more than justice, have not seriously proposed a workable city in which there were no slaves. They do not have to, since they need only think slavery away. Some Stoic slaves have done it, and more Cynics. I could not, if I had been a slave, because the squalor and ugliness and injustice of slavery would bear too heavily upon me at every step I took.

In the Master's Garden, there were free men and freedmen and slaves, but slavery was not ugly or unjust there, because it was, in fact and not merely in theory, wholly disregarded. What is unjust in slavery is that the wrong persons may be slaves, as well as those who in Aristotle's notion, were born to be so. Quintus' mother, Nicandra, was the superior of most of the Roman ladies I knew; and Athamas and Alexis and Dionysius and Tiro are abler and better men than most of those who might have become their masters.

It is not merely vain to imagine a society without slaves, it is, properly speaking, impossible. There are tasks which are degrading and which none the less must be done. It is a pity that Plato did not provide us with some test by which we could recognize at birth those who can do these tasks without harm because they cannot be trained to better ones. Evidently it is hard on men of free and fine natures who suffer the dreadful misfortune of being born slaves or of being enslaved in war. It would be intolerable to contemplate, if it were not for the fact that there are men of humanity who can distinguish between those of their slaves who can be their friends and those who cannot. It is an essential part of our way of life that to make this distinction is for us an imperative duty.

Can this beautiful word, *isonomia,* have any meaning when it is made to apply only to those who had a Roman father and mother, as once it was applied to those who had an Athenian father and mother? I think not. Just as Athamas and Dionysius were born to be free, so it is true that many men born free and Roman, have the qualities and hearts of slaves. I think that Lucius Crassus was right when he said that the old Roman state in which men of birth and property had power, but not all power, was a state in which it was less likely that our lives would be controlled by brutal and violent men, than the state proposed by Gracchus and Marius. That greater likelihood weighs much with me.

And in Athens, when I had become fully and completely conversant with the teaching of our Master, I saw things in a clearer light. The choice demanded of me was not really between one form of the state or the other. These matters are pleasant and profitable to discuss—and endless. What really was presented to us, was a struggle for power between powerful men, men who knew no higher satisfaction than the sense of managing others. The captain of a troop of twenty, is, I suppose, the greatest of the twenty. I have seen such men puffed up inordinately for no greater distinction. What must be the sense of exaltation on the part of a man who is the acknowledged superior of ten thousand thousands?

The Greeks translate our title of imperator by the word *autokrator,* the man who rules by himself alone. Whether this autokrator shall be named Marcus Antonius or Gaius Caesar, will soon be known, though not by me. And to have such power is evidently worth any sacrifice because any and every sacrifice has been made for it.

I, who saw the autokrator, Gaius, at close range and who knew intimately both of the men between whom the choice lies for the next generation, I can only wonder why something should be sought with eagerness and ferocity by men who have no clear use for it when they achieve it. I have seen men hold power and act as if they had never realized till then that power meant the capacity to do something. It seemed almost as if they looked around with desperate indecision for something to do with what they had been at such pains to acquire.

I certainly should not wish to be an autokrator. If I could gratify my real desire, I should prefer to be, like that same Persian, Otanes, of whom Herodotus tells, neither ruler nor ruled. Since that cannot be, I should like, at least, to step as nearly aside as is feasible, while the contest is at its hottest. It is only chance that has saved me from being dragged into it and being torn to pieces by it.

Cicero left the party of the people when he became consul and found that he could not control the clamor for place and profit that every partisan success brings with it. He had long found the democratic association highly distasteful. I had left it much earlier, impelled by no outward pressure, but as a rationally contemplated choice.

I have rejected power. I have foregone glory. Sometimes I think with a pang of poignant regret of the days at Arpinum when we dreamed much of power and glory and when, in Gaius Marius, I thought I had found the one permanent friend and companion of my life. It is a foolish emotion. As well regret my youthful suppleness and strength, or anything else that is past and irrevocably gone.

Quintus indicates that it is time to stop dictating. He has become an exacting master. However, I submit willingly. I do not really mind being ruled by affection.

95

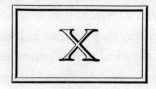

M Y NABATAEAN, LYSANIAS, has proved the most persistent of those who did me the honor of supposing that I had either the power or the desire to help change the face of the world. He has visited me three times. Every time he began with the same kind of indirection. In his soft purring Greek he spoke of tapestries or Corinthian ware or statues or wandering thaumaturgs and brought the conversation by a series of finely shaded transitions to King Malchus and how valuable an ally he would be for Agrippa and Caesar. It has been very amusing to both Quintus and me to watch the shifting of subjects until we got to the primary purpose for which he was sent to Rome.

Very often I have only half listened to him while I watched his face. He is a fine-looking man of over sixty. Like most of his people he wears a beard, which is gray but still noticeably streaked with black. When he turns to one side, his high brow and well-modelled nose give him the appearance of great dignity and sensitiveness. About his hair he has a linen band and he prefers the desert fashion of sitting cross-legged on a cushion rather than on a chair.

His voice is low and pleasant. He rarely moves his body while he is speaking or listening, and when he rises to go it is always with the air of deep gratitude for the courtesy extended to him. One would never know, from his manner, that if he returns to Petra without succeeding in his embassy, Malchus will probably put him to death. Yet he is going back to Malchus although he might have a better chance for his life if he betrayed Malchus to Herodes or Cleopatra, after he has failed in helping Malchus betray Antonius to Caesar.

His attendants are fascinating. I have asked details about them. It seems they are Nubians. At any rate, they came to the great slave market in Arsinoë from the country far up on the Nile. If ever there were men who might properly be called Ethiopians, it would be these Nubians. I have never before seen such shining and glistening black faces although there are dark-skinned and black-skinned men enough in Rome and many more in Alexandria. And their faces become even more shining when they smile and their large white teeth flash at me.

They bow very low to me if they are in the atrium when I come in, but they do not prostrate themselves as the slaves of Archelaus of Cappadocia did. The Cappadocians have been taught this degrading gesture by the Persians who once were their masters. I noticed that the Nubians treat me with greater deference than they do their own master, Lysanias, who speaks to them and deals with them rather familiarly, although they are bought slaves and not houseborn. He speaks to them in his native language which sounds like a dialect of the Syrian speech I heard in Damascus and Berytus, and of which I know a few words. They have, however, a smattering of Greek, enough to exchange a few pleasantries with my slaves.

What interested me especially was that Lysanias said they are almost the only slaves he possesses and that Malchus has only

97

a few more. This is not because the Nabataeans are poor. On the contrary, we should call them very rich and the king particularly has so large a store of golden objects of all varieties that not only Marcus Crassus, who wanted the gold, but even Verres, who wanted the workmanship, would have exulted in a chance to plunder him. And if Lysanias is telling me the truth, another Roman, Lucullus himself, would have been a most appropriate host or guest of Malchus, since eating and drinking seem to be, besides horsemanship and camel-races, the chief forms of diversion of the king and the Nabataean nobles.

Yet, with all that, they have few slaves. They take care of their own persons, groom their own horses and camels and even prepare their food themselves. Only the hardest, most irksome or most unpleasant tasks are performed by slaves and these slaves are not treated as merchandise. They are almost never sold. Once acquired they become members of the household, even more fully than they do with us or with most of the Greeks. Except among the nobles, a man will give his daughter to one of his slaves as readily as he would to the son of a free neighbor.

As far as the two Nubians are concerned, they are in a very special position. They were bought by Lysanias rather as craftsmen than as personal servants. Their craft, I admit, does not interest me, but it is of importance in Petra and Rome. They are skillful cooks, it seems, extraordinarily skillful. Just before he left Rome, with a quiet resignation in my decision not to interfere that impressed me more than all his arguments, Lysanias smilingly confided to me the fact that he had brought them along for the particular purpose of preparing a dinner for Maecenas or Agrippa or me—a dinner that would make Malchus' offers more acceptable. He never was admitted to Maecenas' house and Agrippa was away. On me, the talents of his Nubians were, of course, lost from the beginning. I have always

98

dined sparely, and in the last few weeks, I have scarcely dined at all.

I have thought much of Lysanias and whether Malchus will spare him in spite of the failure of his embassy. And I have also thought about the Nubians and the remote, almost mythical country from which they came and which, except for them, no one I know has ever seen. I wish I could have spoken to them.

I am sorry that Agrippa was not here. True, it would have been awkward for him to be seen in communication with Lysanias. Rumor and gossip busy themselves with everything he does and in twenty-four hours it might have been known all over Rome that he had received a Nabataean envoy. After all, he had been close to Marcus Antonius. But he would have been delighted to see the Nubians and he would have found somewhere a Syrian to act as interpreter. There are Syrians in great numbers in Rome. In fact Agrippa makes a special point of acting as patron to many Syrians and Jews.

I have never known any one so excited about strange peoples and places as Agrippa. If he had free choice and if conditions permitted it, he would travel over the face of the earth like Herodotus and Hanno and Eudoxus and Artemidorus or many another traveller, and pick curiously over the odds and ends of things he could find. But principally, I think, he would like to watch the peoples themselves, all of them, to talk to them and listen to them. I believe Agrippa would have cared very little about putting these things down in a book, either to inform the world or for the satisfaction of writing. He is, first and most of all, curious. And secondly, he has an actual fondness for human beings in general, the same kind of fondness that some men have for horses. They interest him and amuse him and the more widely they differ from the persons he sees about him daily, the more he is interested and amused.

99

Agrippa urged Pollio to have painted or engraved on one of the sides of his library a map of the world, its various countries and seas and rivers and particularly that part of it around the sea as far as the Roman authority extends. He has had such a chart designed for him by a Greek geographer, a friend of our friend Theophanes, and this chart is the largest I have ever seen, much larger than the chart of Eratosthenes, about the correctness of which there are a great many doubts.

I have seen the globe which Crates long ago made and said was the shape of the earth. It has two great bands of water, two oceans, which separate it into four equal parts. Only one quarter, Crates thought, is inhabitable, and that, of course, is where we live. Crates was a Stoic and the Stoics have taken the spherical shape of the earth to be their private and special doctrine. Of course, it fits into the scheme of a universe in which one sphere is inside another. It is very neat mathematically and for all we can tell, quite true.

Agrippa, who is not very much interested in philosophy and has no special fondness for the Stoics, is rather fond of this notion of theirs. Not, however, for the sake of mathematics, but because his imagination is stirred by the thought of there being lands beyond the lands we have ever heard of, below and in back and in front of the habitable region.

As a matter of fact, Agrippa has declared quite justly that he sees no reason why only one quarter of the globe marked off by our oceans should be habitable. And if the other three also have persons living on them, what sort of people are they, these Perioecians and Antoecians and Antipodians?

"Well," I once said to him, "you know what some people say they are like. One-eyed giants, headless monsters with fifty hands, and mouths in their bellies, people who walk upside down, as the Antipodians obviously must, if they are on the other side of us."

Agrippa smiled and shook his head.

"I'll wager they are not like that at all. Probably they will be found to be very like us."

"One could easily find out," I said. "Take a fleet of ships and sail west or east. West, I should suggest. The ocean on the west is right outside the Pillars, only a few weeks' sail. On the east, no one has as yet found it."

"Be careful," said Agrippa, "I might follow your advice. But no," he went on, "no, I don't think I should sail west. Not, at any rate, until I had got a little further east than any one has reached so far."

"As far as Taprobane?" I asked.

"Farther," he said. "To the Seres."

The Seres are often in Agrippa's mind, principally, of course, because we have never seen them, neither he nor I. I have known persons who have seen them in Bactria and have even dealt with them. And I still have some of the fabric that they weave out of the threads of a worm which must be like the many spinning worms about us; a worm, however, which thrives nowhere else. The fabric I have is a very soft and delicate cloth and is already badly torn. The eastern merchants value it highly.

As far as I know, there has never been a Ser in Rome, or even in Antioch or Alexandria. But according to all accounts they are a great and populous nation beyond India and Bactria and Scythia, and have great cities and buildings. They cultivate their lands and build ships and do work in metal and wood and stone, as well as we do or better. But unlike us, especially unlike Agrippa, they do not seem to be curious. Else, surely, some traveller or merchant or envoy from them would have reached our sea.

Some of the accounts declare that they look more like us than the Nubians do. They are dark, but not so dark as the Ethiopians or the Arabs or many African nations. They must be strange enough looking, even if most of the stories about them are not true. I am quite certain that it is not true that they have triangular eyes and no noses. Men are the same kind of animal all over the world, despite their differences, Seres and Nubians and Italians and Gauls and Greeks and Germans and Moors.

What is it that makes all of us men and by that fact makes us different from horses and dogs and apes, much as we resemble the last, as old Ennius said long ago? Our reason, say the Stoics, which is itself a minute little part of the Divine Reason that animates and controls the whole world. This tiny particle goes back to its source whenever any one dies.

If our reason is something different from our soul, I do not know what it can be, and if it is, as we Epicureans think, merely a finer and subtler and more intricate disposition of the atoms of our souls than is found in the souls of brutes, I cannot see how one can make so sharp a distinction as we do between brutes and ourselves. Horses and dogs seem to know what they are doing and what they want and don't want just as well as we do.

Is it only that we have got a somewhat better reason than theirs, so that my reason can be said to be better than my Cappadocian gate-keeper's, just as our Master's was better than mine is, and the Cappadocian's is better than that of his mastiff? One could make a long series in scale after scale, and while there might be many disputes, we should pretty well agree that there are more rational and less rational men and that the least rational man is not so far removed from the most rational brute. Our foresight and our purpose are not better than theirs, not even our success in using our foresight to protect ourselves or to feed ourselves. But we have, I believe, much better memories than they have, and that makes of men animals that can be civilized and of the brutes, animals that cannot be.

I should say that when Hesiod said the Muses were the children of Memory, he had the same thing in mind. It is only by remembering that we can retain anything out of the flux of things about us and only by retaining something that we can make a single thing out of our lives. If it were not for that there would be only a succession of dissolving images in our experience. We could hold a little of what went before, as I suppose even brutes do, and we could foresee a little of what was coming. But being men, and not brutes, we can go so far back that we can rearrange the things that stay in our mind and can play with them and make beautiful things out of them. Or if not always beautiful, at any rate interesting and amusing things.

So, I think man is the remembering animal and not merely the featherless, two-legged animal, and that our souls become human because the images they receive last longer than those which brutes receive. And since everything is in movement around us and within us, reason is only another way of rearranging those images in patterns and in a rhythm or in some other fashion. If memory did not make them cling to our souls, there would be nothing to arrange, however rhythmically or regularly the atoms of our souls moved about. The short-memoried animal that we call a brute has not enough images clinging to his soul to make a pattern out of.

And that is why men can have things in common and men and brutes, however much they live together and however fond we get of our dogs and horses, cannot, after all, have a great deal in common. These creatures are near us, they see what we do, they accompany our steps and there is no lack of affectionate attempts on the part of both, I fancy, to understand each other. But we cannot count on their memory. They remember so little compared to what we remember and they do not remember the same things. There is nothing to base our intercourse on. No day adds anything for them to the day that went before it, and no experience common to us both can be used to make a pattern with another common experience.

It is quite too bad, since our hearts go out to them, because of the very care we take of them, and the games we play with them. And even if their devotion to us is the devotion of a dog, their cringing submission and their wheedling adoration are pleasant in beasts while they would be disgusting in men. Our dogs are too near us to be playthings and too remote from us to be friends.

But it does not follow that those who have most in common with us are most likely to be our friends. My sister, Pomponia, was my closest relation and we resembled each other in features a great deal. Yet our communication was slight and unsatisfactory. We did not like the same things or the same people, nor did the same impulses stir us. I did all I could to support her and protect her, and she never failed in her duty to me. Our affection for each other was real, but it was not warm.

It was the same with my cousins Marcus and Lucius, and their sons of the same names. They are reputable and quiet persons who follow my lead in most matters and treat me as the head of the family. I have no reason to complain of anything they do or have done. Yet I take little pleasure in their company and I cannot suppose they take much in mine. We are kinsmen without being friends just as Pomponia was my sister without being my friend. It is not enough to owe each other duties and to perform them.

That we are kinsmen means that we are descended from the same ancestors, we are plants of the same seed. And that is evident often enough in the forms of our bodies or the expression of our faces. And as our bodies and our souls are of the same stuff it must be that the seeds of the two grow differently within us and make of brothers of one blood persons quite different in character, even if often very much alike in appearance.

Just what this growth is and how things grow and why things grow, both in the case of animal seeds or vegetable seeds, I cannot understand, although I have read much about it, and although, since Aristotle and Theophrastus, men have watched the process closely and have speculated a great deal concerning it. It is a puzzling and mysterious business. And just as difficult to understand is how or when or why the first seeds from which we all sprang, or for that matter any other group of living things, came into existence.

That human beings are in some way akin I well believe. Any one of the stories of the first ancestors of men is as good as any other. They all merely show that we cannot imagine the human race as originating except from a single pair or at most a small number of such pairs. I suppose we can disregard the stories of the gods that begot human offspring or those stories which describe men springing full-grown from the earth or arising from stones miraculously transformed into our shape. But where the first pair or pairs came from eludes our imagination. Somehow, we must take them for granted.

That would mean that we are children of common parents— all of us, Seres and Nubians and Romans. And if we are we cannot very well refuse to admit the obligation which our common humanity imposes on us, as real as the obligation brother owes to brother, or citizen to citizen. It is a mutual obligation and we owe it only to those who recognize a similar obligation to us. In Homer, it is only the inhuman Polyphemus or the brutal Laestrygones who do not recognize it at all, and although in ancient times our ancestors had the same word for the friendly stranger and the hostile stranger, we have long got beyond that. We think of people who kill or enslave suppliant or harmless strangers as ferocious savages not different essentially from wolves or beasts of prey.

Yet, while our common humanity creates a real bond, it is a bond of duty, not necessarily of love or friendship. Those whom we love are bound to us for reasons that bear no ratio to what we have in common. Doubtless it is a combination of many accidents that makes men fond of each other. I have not been able to discover why some of my associates and comrades were dearer to me than others. And of course they were not all my friends in the same degree, nor were they always and under all occasions equally my friends. Not even Marcus Cicero.

Of the three comrades of my youth, Gaius Marius, Lucius Torquatus, and Marcus, I think I should have to admit that when we first learned to know each other, Marcus was probably the one I was least attached to and Marius the one I loved most. The course of events took Marius from me early and from Torquatus I soon became separated by complete diversity of interest and activity. With Marcus Cicero, on the contrary, my association became daily closer and more intimate and it was in this association that I hope I realized most fully the finest of the doctrines of our Master, that friendship is the last and highest achievement of human wisdom.

We rarely spoke of friendship, Marcus and I. At any rate I avoided it as a topic for discussion, although it was a rather popular theme, especially among Stoics. And so many of our

106

friends were Stoics. Cicero himself did not escape the contagion. It was quite natural that he should write a book about friendship and inevitably when he did, it would be a book like so many other books on virtues and vices more or less in the approved style of definition and distinction. This is true friendship and that is not. This is compatible with friendship and that other thing contradicts it. That is more or less the tone of Theophrastus' book on friendship and even more the Stoic method as in the treatise of Chrysippus. Both these books Cicero had read and both he followed in his own little treatise. And of course there are many others. As I say, it is something of a favorite topic for philosophers, even, alas, for schoolboys.

Nonetheless I was pleased when Cicero dedicated his book on friendship to me and suggested in his preface that Gaius Laelius in whose mouth he puts his discussion was really speaking for me. It was a great compliment. The friendship of Scipio Aemilian and Laelius is proverbial among us, and the two men themselves, although I knew persons well who were their intimates, have almost become legendary. I do not think, however, that I am the least like Laelius, nor was Cicero—I am afraid he would have been offended to read this—very much like Scipio Aemilian. Of one thing I am quite sure. I do not think about friendship as Laelius is represented as thinking in Cicero's book. He is made to speak a little too much like the Stoics whose pupil he was, although on the whole the book has charm and dignity and is much closer to reality and experience than any of the models that Cicero had before him.

There is just a little too much in all these books about the advantages of having friends and the disadvantages of being without them and a little too much, even, about the qualities that men should have who are selected as our friends. The proper Stoic doctrine is undoubtedly that no one except a perfectly good man can be a friend at all, and evidently there must be at least two perfectly good men in the association. That is a large number, for perfectly good men. What is absent in all these books—except here and there—is any suggestion of the fact that friendship has much more to do with warmth of feeling than it has with accuracy of definition and with fullness of enumeration. Cicero has kept enough of this glow in his book to make it rank far above even such discussions as that of Aristotle in the book he wrote for Nicomachus.

We do not select our friends as much as we suppose we do. Chance throws us among a large number of persons, but still a limited number. And of these it is chance again which makes it possible to establish with any two or three or ten or twenty, sufficient bonds to make a real affection possible. It happens sooner with some persons than with others, sooner at some times than at others. We are more predisposed—no one really knows how or why—under certain conditions than under others. But a predisposition is necessary. I do not believe that a deliberate selection of a friend on the basis of qualities treated and examined by experience, will be likely to result in friendship, though it will doubtless do very well for a colleague in a magistracy or a partner in a business enterprise.

We take each other with our imperfections and we do not reject each other because our imperfections are more serious or more numerous than we at first supposed. Besides, it is a matter of degree, and none of the empty categories of those who classify these things can help us much to understand them.

Of course, it is not only philosophers who have made friendship an unreal thing, half mathematics and half fog. Poets and popular legends have had their share in this. The stories of the heroic pairs, of Damon and Pythias, of Achilles and Patroclus, of Harmodius and Aristogeiton, have been a little mischievous.

108

Many men have given their lives for their friends, and have suffered much to spare them suffering. And of profuse generosity in such cases we know a great many examples. But soldiers have done as much for a chance comrade in arms, and men without much warmth have given heavily of their own without hope of return, out of a sense of obligation. These are all fine and noble things to do, whoever does them, and that friends will often do them is certain. But it is not in that alone that friendship is manifested. Perhaps not even chiefly in that.

I have often, like everybody else, wished to be alone at times. Indeed, I can remember many hours in which solitary meditation was a real joy and the presence of any one else, even of Atticula or Marcus, would have been a slight disturbance. I do not think we can live without such hours, and it is likely that most men have fewer of them than they need. But they do not take us to the heights on which the Master lived habitually in his garden, when, surrounded by those he loved, he could express his thoughts and feelings and know that he was understood.

That is what we need most of all, affection and understanding. For most of us, of course, need correction by the presence of our friends. Even Epicurus did. He did not live like Pythagoras, and utter oracles to his adoring worshippers, oracles which they were to accept without criticism or discussion. For nearly all men, the presence of our friends, if we are quite open and honest with them, is more than a means of expression; it is our chief means of learning.

It is excessively hard to be quite open. I have never completely achieved it except when I was young and then with Gaius Marius alone. Only then, it seems to me, did I quite reach what I always strove for: the feeling that in speaking to my friend I need check nothing that came to my mind to say, that there were no prejudices to disarm, no excessive sensibility that might be wounded, that I might speak as freely as if I were alone.

Of course the point was that I might speak as if I were alone and yet not be alone. I was present doubly there, sure of the understanding and affection of Marius, as he was sure of mine. We did not agree on everything. I think we disagreed on more things than has been the case with many who were far less my friends. Nor were there instances lacking in which we were at cross purposes, cases in which each misunderstood what the other was saying. There were moments even of heated disagreements. But there were few of them. Unfortunately we were young when we separated forever. Would our friendship have lasted as long as mine and Cicero's did? There is no way of knowing.

Most of the time, even with our friends, we are acting roles. We know that there is a definite character which our friends assume for us and we fall into the part and try to give a consistent presentation. Besides, there is, except among perfect friends, a slight tone of rivalry. We wish just a trifle to surpass the persons before us. Every dialogue is something of a contest.

That is what friendship should not be, and to the degree it gets rid of this, it fulfills itself. In my friendship with Marcus Cicero, there was generally no trace of this rivalry, but there was not quite the complete openness between us that there should have been. When I think of him, I cannot escape the admission that he was readier to be open than I was. I wish it had not been so. It is humiliating to realize that it was I rather than he who fell short of what we both recognized as the highest condition of friendship and its real fruition.

XI

MY HOUSE is in a state of turmoil. It is raining and I
have therefore been compelled to retire to the library
with Dionysius and the copyists. However, I keep the doors
open and I can see from my chair a great deal of running to
and fro, and can hear Quintus' sharp commands and the evident agitation in his voice. He is quite excited, of course. I do
not blame him. It would be strange if he did not show some
disturbance. Caesar has announced that he would visit me
tomorrow.

It is very likely this will be the last visit I shall ever receive
from him. It is by no means the first, but his visits have become
rarer and rarer and, I am afraid, heavier and more difficult for
both of us. It is not quite his fault. He has tried very hard to
make it seem that he is a mere private citizen visiting another
private citizen. In dress he is indistinguishable from any other
Roman senator. He comes unattended except by a few friends
and two slaves. He does not even take lictors with him as he
might well do by virtue of his official position, since he is consul again this year, and as a member of the Commission would
by that fact alone be entitled to the full honors of the highest

III

magistracy. I have visited and been visited by petty princes and kings in Asia, any one of whom would be willing to prostrate himself in the dust before Caesar and every one of whom was arrayed in a splendor and moved with a pomp infinitely greater than his.

For all that, he becomes a more and more difficult guest with each visit and as I gather from our other friends, he becomes so not only to me but to all of us. The very fact that the lictors do not accompany him, instead of relieving his visit of the sense of his power and authority, seems to increase it. Not for one second can any one forget that the lictors are not there and that they have been deliberately left behind.

Caesar is just thirty-one, having been born in Marcus Cicero's eventful consulship. He is six years older than Alexander was when he conquered Persia and just about as old now as Alexander was when he died, the undisputed master of the East. He died drunk, this lord of the East. Of one thing we may be sure, Caesar Octavian will not die drunk.

I find him a little harder to understand than all the other men I have known who were at all like him, the men, I mean, to whom power was as essential as breathing and whose energies had no free rein except when they were managing large numbers of other men. They were all in some degree exuberant persons, Sulla, Marius, Marcus Antonius, the Dictator Caesar, the older Lepidus, Lucius Cinna. The force of their souls showed itself in their bodies. Indeed, it spilled over. It could be said of Caesar the Dictator that he was never quite motionless. If nothing else, his eyes moved. In fact, his glance darted continuously about him. One would almost say it flashed in all directions.

And yet, I usually found myself perfectly at ease with the older Caesar, while recently I have not been quite at ease with this young man who succeeds to Caesar's name, and, as far as we of the West are concerned, to his power. Whether he will succeed to all his power will depend on that imminent struggle which it seems impossible to avoid and which may bring with it the ruin of all the forms of civilized life that we possess. I sometimes think that this imminence has increased the strange disturbance I feel in the presence of Caesar Octavian.

But it is, I am sure, not wholly or even chiefly that reason. The immobility which his face can assume whenever he wishes, the perfect composure of manner he usually exhibits and which his rival, Marcus Antonius, could not simulate, even if he tried—these give intercourse with him a difficulty that I never found before. I can imagine myself being the victim of a furious burst of rage from Antonius, but I should know what caused his rage and why it was vented on me. I am not sure I or anybody else would always be able to explain Caesar's anger, and for that reason it is more of a thing to dread.

Not that I have any reason to dread it. Even if Caesar disliked me, I cannot see what harm he or anyone else could cause me. Dionysius of Syracuse himself or Phalaris or any other legendary example of an insane tyrant could hardly do more in respect to me than expedite somewhat a solution that every week brings appreciably nearer. And if Caesar were a Phalaris on a hitherto unexampled scale, he could do no more. Circumstanced as I am, I am really not under the power of the master of a dozen legions, the permanent imperator, the man whose will no man in Italy or Gaul or Spain or Africa will venture to oppose or contradict.

But Caesar is no Phalaris. Quite the contrary. I should not call him a kind man, but he is certainly not inhumane. He has little of the genial warmth of his granduncle or the demonstrative affection of his rival, but it would be wrong to think of him as cold or unresponsive to friendship or without generous impulses. Like the Dictator, he is fond of women, but unlike him, he is a little furtive in his pleasures. Antonius is quite justified in questioning Caesar's right to condemn him for incontinence. That he loves his wife Livia I have no doubt. But it is equally certain that their union is a marriage of temperaments as much as of erotic attraction. At any rate, Livia is of the same stamp as the many purposeful Romans with whom I have been associated all my life, and if she had been a man, she would doubtless have been Caesar's rival, just as being a woman, it is quite natural that she should be Caesar's wife.

It is this matter of openness of disposition in which the contrast between our Caesar and the Dictator is most apparent. The Dictator was not above deviousness when it suited his purposes. He could dissemble when he wished, but he almost gave you warning that he was doing so. When he attempted in the Senate to save the lives of Lentulus and Cethegus and the other associates of Catilina, he solemnly declared that he did so because their crimes deserved a severer punishment than death. But every one of us must have been aware that he knew more of the plans of the conspirators than any other man in Rome except Crassus. Lentulus went to his death without betraying him. Indeed, he had little chance to. If he had, Caesar—the elder Caesar—would have sneeringly defied Cicero and the Senate to prove his complicity.

But ordinarily the Dictator left no one in doubt as to his intentions and his plans. We can scarcely say that of Caesar Octavian. His intentions, I think, are clear. But how he means to carry them out, I should say no one knows, except Maecenas and Agrippa, and these do not know everything nor does one know all that the other does.

To Maecenas, I believe, Caesar is as open as he can possibly be. And I do not doubt—no one can doubt—his sincere friend-ship for Maecenas. Nor for Agrippa, either, for that matter, but his attachment to Agrippa is not as close as it is to Maecenas. It is a little strange that it should be so. If sobriety is a charac-teristic of Caesar's, the opposite is very nearly the characteristic of Maecenas, who takes few things seriously, least of all himself, and scarcely even the Roman state which is almost the one ab-sorbing passion of our young perpetual imperator.

The question has arisen more than once among us, both in Caesar's presence and when Agrippa and I were alone, whether it would be possible to divide the Sea into an East and West, and let Antonius reign in Alexandria as a king of kings, if he likes, while Octavian remains in Rome, the first citizen and first magistrate of the city which wishes to be the patron and not the mistress of all the peoples of the West. There would be no civil war then and the indignant iambics which Quintus Ho-ratius wrote and which he read to our applause more than a month ago would be unnecessary.

Apparently that cannot be. Two men and two cities, Agrippa said, might live together as friends. Two empires cannot. And that seems to be because an empire is not a real thing, since most of those who compose it cannot have any harmony of wishes or interest or enough similarity to make them even par-tially understand each other. If the only unity they have is that they fear the power of one master man or mistress city, that unity will end when they cease to fear. And fear, it seems, is no more permanent an emotion than joy or sorrow.

Therefore there must be one empire throughout all the shores of the Sea and not two, and while Antonius and Octavian might share the rule of it as colleagues, or partners, they cannot divide it, like partners who have agreed to separate.

Perhaps. I accept Agrippa and Maecenas and Caesar as wiser

men and more competent in these things than I am. But while I yield to their arguments, they have not convinced me. And in fact, I suspect that the real reason is somewhat different, and more practical.

Maecenas phrased it in the way that is usual with him. "What Caesar means," he said—Caesar was not present—"is that we must suppress Homer. As long as people read how glorious it is to kill each other in large batches, life will be precarious."

"It is impossible," said Agrippa, "to eliminate war. Neither Plato nor Zeno thought it was feasible for ordinary communities of ordinary men. I say nothing about their own private and peculiar communities."

"Oh," said Maecenas laughing. "War is not to be eliminated. It is to be a privilege of the governing people. We Romans must go on fighting with each other to keep ourselves in practice. It is the other tribes that must get out of the habit."

"And how is it to be done?" I asked.

"By the fact that the Romans alone will have the means of making war. Or should have."

"That is fear again."

"Yes, but it is fear of one and not of two. If there are two, some group will play off one against the other, and we shall have general war once more."

Caesar has confirmed the statement that to keep the peace is all that can justify the supremacy of Rome. It was Cicero's notion too. Indeed this phrase that Rome is the patron and not the mistress of the peoples of our world is Cicero's. But to Cicero it was a Rome of magistrates and senate and comitia, not the Rome of a monarch. And Caesar protests that he too wishes a Rome of senate and magistrates and comitia. He declares he would accept neither the title nor the powers of a monarch.

Caesar has never in so many words spoken of the conflict

116

with Antonius as inevitable. He has referred to it as a possibility he regretted but which he hoped could be avoided. For his part he declares he can live in perfect association and amity with Antonius, if Antonius will on his side do his part. Both of them, he says, should lay down their extraordinary powers as members of the Commission—two only are left of the Triumvirate—and return to Rome as private citizens to receive such offices and honors as the Senate and the Roman people wish to bestow on either or both.

No one knows better than Caesar that it is quite impossible for Antonius to accept this offer, that it would be suicidal if he did. And obviously he does not seriously think Antonius will accept. Agrippa and Maecenas have never spoken of the coming conflict except as a thing which is as certain as that the sun will rise. Peace must be maintained by the rule of Rome and for that purpose Rome must be ruled by one man. Neither Maecenas nor Agrippa has much faith in the Senate and the Roman people.

But Rome without the Senate and the Comitia is not Rome, and to many Romans the only reason for preferring Caesar to Antonius must be that Caesar will stay here on the Tiber and Antonius will doubtless prefer the Nile and the tapestries and cushions, the eunuchs and the prostrate or acclaiming rabble of Alexandria and Seleucia, and if he is fortunate, Babylon as well. Yet, if we are to have a monarch perhaps it is more fitting that he should assume the dress and the tone, and the airs of the king of kings, the Son of the Sun, the Favorite of the Moon, or whatever silly title Egyptians and Syrians give their kings, than that he should be clad in a plain woolen toga, and walk among us as a simple citizen, merely having his name the first on our census lists, but otherwise not different from other men in the same class.

This is what makes Caesar's company oppressive. He is so much more than our first citizen, for all that he refuses to be a monarch, that we cannot deal with him as though he were merely one of a class, when we know that he stands above all classes. It was easier to deal with the Dictator who did not mean you to forget that he could wield whatever power he chose, and who had no hesitation in referring to that fact in conversation.

"And who," Maecenas reminded me, "was cut down by Roman senators in the sight of a crowded assembly without a hand raised to defend or avenge him."

It seems, therefore, that we will endure a master who pretends not to be one, but not one who admits that he is. It is very human and very Roman. It does not seem very reasonable.

If I were not a Roman I wonder whether I should think that peace was desirable at the expense of a permanent subordination of my people to the Romans. And this permanent subordination is very much Caesar's notion, as it was Cicero's. That all the peoples of our world should be fused into one community, he neither expects nor desires.

Caesar the Dictator seems to have had some such notion in mind. So, we are told, did Alexander. And so does Antonius, as far as he can be said to have any one purpose since he shifts from one idea to another. All three consistently or half-consistently entertained the hope that one could take these many thousands of thousands of men who live around the Sea and form a single state out of them, make all of them citizens of a single community.

It sounds preposterous, but I am not sure it is quite impossible. It would need the energetic and long-continued directing of a powerful and steady will. The Dictator had it, surely. And Alexander, somewhat less surely. But in any case, the task was too great to be accomplished in the few years either had at his disposal. It needs at least three generations. If it had been accomplished, it would also have needed a different kind of government from any we have known, except in Egypt. It would require prefects and under-prefects, district magistrates reporting to provincial magistrates, a system of accounts that would have dazzled my uncle Quintus, an army of tax-collectors and another army of scribes. Well enough for Egyptians. Caesar is right—our Caesar—in thinking it will not do for Romans.

And that is the choice. A world held openly in check by a single people while this people is itself held covertly in check by a single man, who pretends not to be doing it. Or else a world openly ruled by a monarch, an autokrator, who spends his life and power in the scarcely possible task of welding hundreds of peoples into a single one. I think it is scarcely possible because it needs several generations to do it, assuming it could be done at all, and we cannot reasonably expect that there will be a series of monarchs equally powerful, equally persistent, and equally imaginative to carry it through in successive generations.

Such are our two ways of peace. The former—Caesar Octavian's way, Cicero's way—is more nearly the Roman way. But I share the doubts about it that Agrippa freely admits to me, although he does not declare them to Caesar. I do not think the Rome that Cicero had in mind, the Rome of our traditions, can hold the world in check any longer. And Caesar's method of acting the part of the unseen monarch beneath the mask of the freely elected magistrate cannot be permanent. Sooner or later he must drop the mask. I believe with Agrippa that he could do it safely in spite of the fate of the Dictator. But I believe with Maecenas that whether he could or not, Caesar Octavian is more comfortable with the mask over his features than without it. If he ever dropped it I am convinced the monarchy of Caesar would for the vast majority of the people of

the world—our world—be different from the monarchy of Antonius only in the name of the person who rules by himself
alone. For Greeks and Gauls and Moors it can make very little
difference who appoints their taskmasters and collects their
tribute.

It is a heavy price to pay for peace. An absurd price, if we
asked ourselves why it should be necessary to pay any price.
War is so completely unreasonable.

That, of course, is a commonplace of the schools. To kill one
man is a dreadful crime, if it is done for profit or out of mere
brutal lust of killing. But to kill ten thousand for the purpose of
increasing our revenues or proving our strength is a title to
glory. It is carved on our monuments. It is commemorated with
trophies. It is the theme of hymns and epics. How much would
be left of all that our poets have written if we took war from
them? Should we not have to suppress Homer, as Maecenas
ironically suggests, if we tried to suppress war?

The answers we learned from our teachers are ready enough
to hand. We may well admire our ancestors who roamed the
forests, clad in wolf-hides, and lived on acorns or the uncooked
flesh of the wild ox. We may even sing of their prowess. But
we do not therefore live in forests or munch acorns or run
about in all weathers naked but for a wolf-skin girdle. At least
we do so only at the Lupercalia, and it is quite fitting, as our
Master says, that our religious festivals should make us resemble
the rudest and wildest of our savage ancestors.

And if we can sing about our ancestors without imitating
them why can we not read Homer without sharing his delight
in slaughter or exulting with him when his heroes dash the
blood and brains of their foes into the dust, or when Skamander
is choked with Trojan corpses? Achilles and Ajax speak of their
exploits as no one but a gladiator would speak now. Yet it is

120

hard to see what difference there is between the sack of Troy and the sack of Carthage. Apparently if we do not dress as our savage ancestors did or eat the food they used, we take as much satisfaction as they did in killing.

Still, there is a little difference. The war against Troy had a reason, even if sensible people would hardly call it an adequate one. But when Achilles incidentally destroys Thebes, it is for no reason at all. Nor did Cyrus have any better reason for extending his conquests than the desire to be a greater king than his predecessors.

We at least acknowledge the obligation of finding a reason. When the Dictator Caesar writes of his wars in Gaul, he is at some pains to show that he did no more than protect Roman citizens or Roman allies. I did not find his reasons very convincing. Nor did Cato, who moved in the Senate on one occasion to surrender Caesar to the Usipetes as one who had violated the law of all nations by a wanton attack on a peaceful people. And I do not believe Caesar cared very much whether his reasons sounded sufficient or not. But it is noteworthy that he thought a reason was necessary. The Homeric heroes were quite satisfied with killing with or without a reason.

It is not a great improvement, but it is something. Perhaps, if the monarchy of Caesar or Antonius will give us the habit of peace by compulsion, it may grow into the habit of peace by reason. I scarcely venture to hope it, however.

There is, of course, that other way of peace, the way of reason. It seems remote enough. Plato's city was possible only when philosophers became kings or kings philosophers, and it has been ridiculed because of the patent absurdity of the condition. Yet it is not really absurd. There have been kings who were almost philosophers and there might well be one who was so completely. Evidently, he could not be an Epicurean, but that

121

would not be necessary, and if we accept Plato's premises, not even desirable.

But to make peace permanent—and only a peace of reason would be permanent—not the kings, but the people must be philosophers, or a great many of them. That also is possible. But I see little likelihood of its happening.

Evidently we cannot expect that the Scythians and Germans and the desert Africans would suddenly become rational philosophers even if we of our world did. But a war to protect our frontiers is not the kind of war that can be eliminated. Agrippa is quite right about that. If these tribes can be civilized, there will doubtless be other and wilder tribes beyond them whom it will be their task to drive back on behalf of the civilization they will share with us.

A war for defense is not unreasonable, just as the execution of a pirate is not. But a war among ourselves, among us who do not live in forests as the rivals and comrades of bears and panthers, that is supremely unreasonable and we can hope—alas, we can do no more than hope—that it may one day be apparent that it is unreasonable.

It is not that life is precarious in war that makes peace desirable. In the Garden, we value life, but not for itself. Or rather we do not value it any more than we value the sun or the earth or food and drink. It is one of the conditions of our being. It is not better or worse than anything else. We either are alive or we are not. We cannot estimate whether being alive is better than being dead, because we cannot at the same time know both these conditions or have the sensations of both of them simultaneously. Being dead means knowing nothing and feeling nothing.

We do not fear death, therefore. I, at least, have never feared it. And we do not dread the loss of our property if it is not all taken away, or the loss of power, if we are not deprived of our liberty. If glory, which is merely a word for boasting of superior strength or superior wealth—if that is the purpose of war, many men would surrender power and wealth, if they might retire with their friends where neither power nor wealth is unduly valued.

But it is the incidental destruction of war that makes it a thing to dread. We can only enjoy life because we can remember, and our memories need the concrete things that have been built and written and fashioned before us. Each generation cannot build them up again. War compels us to do that in part; and long-continued war compels us to do it almost completely. We cannot send men out to kill without loosening the impulse to destroy everything they see which they cannot or do not wish to take with them. We should not expect a pack of wolves to discriminate between what they might reasonably rend in pieces and what not.

If we had peace, our imagination could function as a sort of prospective memory. We could count on what we did surviving long enough to be a part of the memory of the next generation. And that is not in the least because it is important to be remembered. What I think of as surviving is not the fame of those who did the work but the work itself. But for the fact that our Master's writings survived and those of his pupils, we should probably not have discovered the way of life he points out nor should we have seen so clearly through the confused flux of our experience. The men of the next generation will be richer than the one before us because they will have the writings of Marcus Cicero and Titus Lucretius. And Marcus Varro's too, although they will go to him for information rather than

123

for stimulation. Besides them there is the likelihood that Vergilius and Horatius and Varius will do fine things, if they are not wiped out by the calamities that war brings with it.

We do not like to build things of sand or of any material that will disappear almost as soon as our handiwork is finished. And the prospect of war makes even the works of poets and sculptors and architects things of sand that crumble to pieces almost as soon as they are made. Only chance allows some things to survive. Who knows whether Homer was the first of poets or the best? There has been so little peace since the sack of Troy. As little as before it.

The consul, Gaius Caesar Octavian, member of the Commission to reorganize the Roman state, perpetual imperator, sacrosanct in person by decree of the Senate, is to pay me a visit tomorrow. He will discuss many things with me. And he will carefully avoid any reference to his official position, to Antonius or to Marcus Cicero. He will speak of peace but not of what he will do to obtain it.

I hope it will be a short visit.

AGRIPPA CAME BACK the day before yesterday, two days earlier than he was expected. And he came to see me almost as soon as he arrived. He was in great consternation. Nepos sent him word that I was in a serious condition. I did not realize how much my looks must have changed in the four weeks during which he was away. He burst into tears as soon as he saw me.

Balbus and Nepos both arrived directly after him. They brought a new physician with them, an Egyptian again, named Phibammon. I will say that he was a far more sensible person than most of his craft. He agrees with me that there is nothing to be done. Drugs and diet may prolong my life a few months, but there is really no chance of my surviving much longer than that under any circumstances.

My will was made long ago. It is very simple. I have not given many directions nor made many conditions. I am forbidden by law to make Atticula the executrix of my will or to leave her more than half of my property. I have observed the law and have made no attempt to evade it, although Cascellius and Trebatius have both shown me how easily it could be evaded. Quintus is co-heir and executor with Agrippa, but not equally, of course. I have provided few legacies and have merely urged Quintus and Agrippa to deal kindly and generously with all those they think have a claim to some share in my property, and to emancipate Alexis and one or two other slaves. The debts which the city of Athens and the colony of Buthrotum owe me are to be cancelled. Dionysius is to have my books and my copyists but is to let my friends and especially Atticula and Quintus pick out whatever books they wish to keep.

It is something of a joke on Dionysius that it is he who will probably have to publish that highly authoritative treatise of Appius Claudius on the evocation of ghosts.

I am aware that I may have to go through several more scenes like the one of yesterday, and that Agrippa and Quintus and Nepos and Balbus will be at me again to persuade me to continue the useless struggle with death. Since their Egyptian has turned out to be a man of sense, they will doubtless dismiss him and unearth some other physician who will make lying promises and assure them and me that I can be cured, if I will surrender myself to his direction. I have no intention of doing so.

My death will hurt five persons who are very dear to me. But it will be a sharp and brief pain, while the prolongation of my agony will be a long continued pain, a physical pain to me and a bitter suffering to those who must watch me suffer. Surely the mere fact that I shall remain alive a little longer is no compensation for that. We can have no real communication—any of us—while I am in that state. By taking almost no food, my limbs and body become weaker daily, but I am not in pain. I find it necessary now to lie in bed continuously, propped up by pillows. But my mind is clear. I can think and talk, if rarely more than an hour or so at a time. After talking a little, I become drowsy and fall asleep. Doubtless, without my being conscious of it, my periods of drowsiness are getting longer and longer. And then, from one of these periods, I shall not awake at all. I shall be dead.

It is nearly sixty years since I read the first book of Epicurus that fell into my hands, his letter to Menoeceus. And it is almost as long since I heard Phaedrus at Athens expound the Cardinal Principles. If I lived to a hundred and more I should never forget the profound impression they made on me. It had almost the effect of an illumination. I have understood life and death from that moment. When the bricks and stones of a house are pulled apart, the bricks and stones are still there, but the house is not. And when the atoms of which I am composed are dissociated, they will continue to exist, but I—who was merely their union—I shall not exist.

It is all so very simple. It does not in the least mean that I never really existed, any more than the debris of a broken house means that there never was a house. On the contrary, I indubitably was and am. Evidently I am made up of many more parts than the hugest house and these parts are more intricately put together than the most cunning mosaic. But that could be said of Erotion, Atticula's Maltese dog, who is licking my hand at this moment, or of any flower in my garden. If to be what I am now means that a separable soul or effigy or ghost or double has been inhabiting my bones and sinews, the same must be said of every blade of grass in the meadow or of every midge that dances in the sunlight.

It is so hard for us to think of emptiness that we make a thing out of it almost as solid as what we must think away to imagine emptiness. It is the same with death which we find ourselves imagining as a different kind of life from the one whose end death is, very much like it, however, both in what was pleasant and what was unpleasant in life itself. And except for the ab-

surdities of Pythagoras, death must be supposed to last forever, just because it is not life, which comes to an end sooner or
later. And endlessness is not merely hard, but impossible, to
imagine.

Both death and infinity are only words for nothing, no life
or no time. To think about nothing is merely not to think.
Those who have fancied a life after death, a shadow-life like the
Hades of most of the Greeks, a life of uninterrupted delight
like that of the son-in-law of Zeus in the Islands of the Blest,
those persons are merely children amusing themselves with
pictures. We do not really need to consider them seriously.

Nor indeed can we seriously talk about those other notions
of our philosophers, who imagine continual circles of existence,
great years of years which repeat each other, so that everything
that happens has happened before and will happen again. Much
better to go back to the doctrine of Zeno of Elea which is that
nothing happens at all and that it merely seems as though it
did. Or perhaps we might try, as the Gymnosophists say, to step
out of the cycle of being and so escape the eternal whirl. Neither
doctrine makes sense. If those who imagine Hades or Tartarus
or the Elysian Fields are playing with pictures, these others are
playing with words. My time for playing with either is running
very short.

Being is nothing else except being. It is not going forward or
upward or moving in a circle. It is nothing that can be described. To describe it we should have to use the meaningless
terms I have mentioned. We should have to speak of stepping
outside of it in order to see it. But we can see one thing clearly.
There is no direction in it. There is no goal to living. Chance,
which marks the flux, turns our life first here and then there,
and whatever direction there can be in life is what we put into
it ourselves. It does not really matter if we are driven by un-

seen forces whether we will or no. To say that things seem to happen, but do not really happen, is only changing the meaning of the word happen. And to say that we do not direct our lives but only think we do, is the same sort of thing. Thinking is directing.

I believe I have directed my life. It would be unspeakably silly for me to say that I have directed it successfully. I have been successful but most of that is due to chance. My wealth was the gift of chance. Doubtless I was more competent in keeping it and in increasing it than other men might have been. But most of the risks that beset it were the results of acts and events with which I had nothing to do, which I could not have prevented or changed. Civil war and accidents, disease and calamities, all these I have known. Other men as wary and as skillful as I was, were destroyed or ruined by them. My success was as much due to chance as the successful resistance of one or two leaves that cling to a tree when a hurricane sweeps through it.

The direction of my life has been in other things. Each situation that faced me provided in some degree the opportunity of following the way of life I had selected. Almost never was the opportunity so obvious and so full that I dared feel I had used it as completely as possible.

Epicurus lived his life in a garden remote from the world. Not, of course, removed from all possibility of disaster. Wars and barbarian invasions might have swept through Athens while he was there, as they had before him and as they did after him. If they had, he would have borne them with equanimity, I am sure. But in any case, he lived the life for which he was fitted and the tasks of which he could admirably perform. He thought out his doctrine there in the Garden and expounded it to his disciples.

And, since Epicurus, others have lived like him, developing and applying and teaching the Master's doctrines. Evidently only a few can do that. And I could never have been of that number.

It would be a poor and barren doctrine if it could be used only by those who taught it or talked about it or contemplated it. Our living is determined by the place and time in which we live and the things that happen around us. We cannot all live in gardens in the suburbs of a city that has ceased to be the capital of an empire and lies outside the stream of political change. But we can deal in our own fashion with whatever happens to us; while we cannot force things to happen differently, our share in them will be what we make it. We must get what satisfaction life can offer us, even if it offers us at certain times and places only the merest drop.

A perfectly wise man will direct his life consistently. He will view his surroundings calmly. He will weigh his motives and estimate the strength of his impulses. Has there ever been so perfectly wise a man? I cannot believe it. Epicurus approached it more nearly than most of those we know about. Marcus Cato was nearer to it than I. Yet both of them fell far short of completely realizing perfection of wisdom. For one thing, many things must be done too quickly to admit of dispassionate reflection at every stage. And for another, it is much harder to weigh and regulate our impulses than philosophers admit in their discussions.

To yield to every impulse is contemptible. The fact that we are rational ought to mean that this is precisely what we do not do. Reason is principally engaged in selecting from our impulses those which it will be more rational to follow. Not to use our reason is as silly as not to use our eyes. It is as though an animal preferred to run on three legs instead of four. We are rational animals, just as we are erect and partially hairless animals. To discard reason is to act like something we are not.

Nor is the use of reason without its own satisfaction and its own thrill of pleasure. I have found in sheer speculation a joy of its own kind, different from and incommensurable with the pleasures of the senses, but thoroughly real for all that. They are neither better nor worse, but of another sort and quality. My life would have been dull and desolate if I had been deprived of the satisfaction of following my impulse to be rational, just as denying myself to all the impulses of sense would not have been a lofty austerity but a foolish self-tormenting like the actions of those Eastern priests who whip themselves with thongs and gash themselves with knives in honor of their god.

The strength of impulses is different in different men and different in the same man at different times. Epicurus taught that those sensual pleasures which seem the most intense, like the pleasure of sexual indulgence, are to be avoided as much as possible. "No man was ever the better for sexual intercourse, and most men have been the worse for it." Not all his followers agreed with him, nor did he insist that they must. But there can be no doubt that he was right in the main. The more violent the impulse is, the greater the danger that we shall yield to it without considering the consequences. And incontinence is the abandonment of reason. It will happen occasionally. It can scarcely help happening sometimes. But no trained and cultivated man will permit incontinence to be the rule of his life.

Our reason in any given case will select, by a standard of its own, the impulses that are to carry us. The impulses themselves are for the most part neither good nor bad. It is what they result in that gives them their quality. Still there are some that seem in themselves fine and some that seem unqualifiedly evil.

I have not always been rational, even when I had intended to

131

be and when I suffered deep mortification because I had not been. I have given vent to silly bursts of anger at small annoyances and yielded lightly to self-indulgences that it would have become me better to forego. But I think that there are two impulses I have succeeded in eradicating, and those are jealousy and cruelty. Unless my memory has become a fawning parasite —memories can do that—I cannot recall a single instance in which I have resented the fact that some one else possessed what I also possessed and valued, or enjoyed what I enjoyed. I have desired many things and attained most of them. What I tried without success to get rarely cost me a pang of real regret.

Perhaps jealousy is only a mean sort of envy, an envy that transfers itself from the thing you desire to the possessor. In that case, it is wrong for me to say that I eradicated it. I cannot remember that I ever felt it, even slightly. In wealth I had so much that only insatiable avarice would have wished for more. And what I should have liked to have and did not possess— Marcus Cicero's richness and fluency and suavity of style, Titus Lucretius' profundity and imagination, Cato's loftiness of spirit —those things I could not have had without becoming a different sort of person. To say that is, I suppose, to say that I never really wanted them. Grown men cannot want things that are obviously unattainable.

And I am glad I rarely if ever felt the impulse to do wanton harm to another person. It ought to be as absurd for a man to boast of his humanity as to boast that he speaks instead of barks. That we have better reasons and longer memories than beasts is what gives us the right to call ourselves men. But that we do more harm to each other than beasts do to beasts, is evident enough and it is equally evident that we do it without reason. We kill each other not for food or for sex-desire, as beasts do, but to glut an independent impulse to cruelty. One may say that the cruelty of beasts is more rational than ours.

The way life is ordered makes it so easy for cruel men to be cruel. It is merely necessary to buy a slave on whom you can pour out your rages when they occur, whom you can strike or abuse as you like, whom you can even kill. He is in a worse condition than a dog, since it is not easy for a slave to run away. He depends for his living on the man who abuses him. Of course there are only a few men who act this way toward their slaves, but there are some, and a great many more deal cruelly with their slaves occasionally, even if only to a slight extent. To kill, to rend, to destroy, to hurt other living things is an impulse in us stronger than it is in dogs and wolves and tigers. It is one of the few impulses for which no good use can be found.

There are, I know, violent and savage slaves just as there are untamable beasts. And among free men there are thieves and cutthroats and pirates. Perhaps the best thing that can be done with them is to put them to death. I am not sure. My Athenian fellow-citizens found out long ago that merely putting all persons to death when they broke the rules of the city did not prevent the rules from being broken. We have found out the same, we Romans, in a wider experience.

I have never seen a man cringe without feeling a shudder of repulsion, a repulsion generally directed to those who made him cringe rather than to him. I have never made any man cringe, not even slaves whom I felt it necessary to punish. Men have fawned on me because they thought me rich and influential. Usually I have despised them for doing so. Often I was as much amused as disgusted. But no man, I think, not even the miserable assassins whom my Epirote steward captured years ago and brought to me for punishment, could have supposed that I took any satisfaction in punishment or that I looked on callously at their wretchedness and suffering.

It may well be that it was no merit of mine that I found it possible to root out this feeling in me. There are men, not naturally cruel, who, doubtless, find the impulse at times much stronger than it ever was in me. Those many men whom I knew so well, so many of whom were my friends, were for the most part not cruel in the ordinary acts of their lives. Perhaps Sulla had more of it than the others. But what they chiefly sought was a gratification of their sense of superiority. They were men of powerful energies in almost all matters. They loved action and loved it most when it affected other men. I suppose that involves a little love of cruelty, because it requires beating down resistance and enjoying the sensation of trampling on a fallen opponent.

I have had little desire to command other men or to impose my will on them. And not having it, I wonder whether I can estimate properly those who did have it, to whom it was indispensable. Their vigor expressed itself best when they were driving men before them, and that cannot be done unless it is somewhat mingled with cruelty. We who do not have it must contrive to live somehow in a world in which cruelty is prevalent, just as travellers over dangerous routes must manage to protect themselves as well as they can from robbers and wild beasts. It is not necessary to travel to Taprobane or the Seres or the sources of the Nile to meet dangerous situations.

Atticula is with me every day. Agrippa assures me he has not told her how imminent my death is. When she is with me, she is gaiety itself. A little too obviously. She has been reading to me—Plato, chiefly, carefully avoiding the *Phaedo*. I am trying very hard to realize that I must not speculate on what might happen to her, if there should be many more civil wars and more proscriptions. My mind ran back to that morning during the Terror not quite eleven years ago when, before dawn, Quintus and Pillia and Atticula and I, led by Volumnius' slave, Sthenelus, crept out of the back gate of my garden and hurried by unfamiliar streets and paths to the house of Volumnius. Light was just breaking and we saw muffled figures here and there, fleeing as we were fleeing, most of them, poor wretches, with less success. The recollection was so painful that I started visibly and frightened Atticula. But we continued the pretense that I was ailing a little and would be completely recovered soon.

This morning even that pretense broke down. She read the speech to me that Plato imagined Socrates using to his judges. She faltered when she began the last sentence and could not go on. I recited it to her and she fell sobbing in my arms. Agrippa and Quintus wished to lead her away. But I forbade it.

"And now," says the Platonic Socrates, "it is time to go; for me, to death, and for you, to life. Which of us goes to the better thing, no one knows but God."

I think Plato was wrong. The gods do not know. Nor do I.

DRAMATIS PERSONAE

I
HISTORICAL PERSONS

FAMILY AND FRIENDS OF ATTICUS

1. Titus Pomponius Atticus (after his adoption, officially known as Quintus Caecilius), 110-32 B.C.

2. Atticula, his daughter. (Atticula is a nickname. Her official name was Pomponia and, later, Caecilia.)

3. Pillia, wife of Atticus, daughter of Quintus Celer (No. 9).

4. Quintus, freedman of Atticus.

5. Pomponia, sister of Atticus, wife of Quintus Cicero (No. 17).

6. Quintus Caecilius, the elder, uncle and adoptive father of Atticus.

7. Marcus Vipsanius Agrippa, minister and friend of Octavian, husband of Atticula.

8. Agrippina, his daughter, affianced as a child to Tiberius (No. 27).

9. Quintus Pillius Celer, father of Pillia, adherent of Caesar.

10. Lucius Cornelius Balbus, friend of Atticus and of Cicero.

11. Cornelius Nepos (first name unknown), friend and biographer of Atticus.

12. Gaius Trebatius ⎫
13. Aulus Cascellius ⎬ lawyers, friends of Atticus
14. Aulus Ofilius ⎭

15. Publius Volumnius, Epicurean philosopher, friend of Atticus.

CICERO AND HIS FAMILY

16. Marcus Tullius Cicero, the orator.

17. Quintus Tullius Cicero, his brother.

18. Marcus Tullius Cicero, the younger, son of Marcus (No. 16).

19. Quintus Tullius Cicero, the younger, son of Quintus (No. 17).

20. Marcus Tullius Tiro, freedman and biographer of Marcus (No. 16).

21. Tullia, daughter of Marcus (No. 16).

22. Gaius Calpurnius Piso, her first husband.

THE CAESARIAN FAMILY

23. Gaius Iulius Caesar, the Dictator.

24. Gaius Iulius Caesar Octavian, nephew and adopted son of the Dictator, later called Augustus.

25. Livia, his wife.

138

26. Marcus Livius Drusus, brother of Livia.

27. Tiberius Iulius Caesar (born Tiberius Claudius Nero), step-son of Octavian (No. 24) and adopted by him. Affianced husband of Agrippina (No. 8).

28. Gaius Cilnius Maecenas, adviser of Octavian, patron of letters.

YOUNGER CONTEMPORARIES OF ATTICUS—ANTI-CAESARIANS

29. Marcus Iunius Brutus

30. Gaius Cassius Longinus } the "Liberators"

31. Decimus Iunius Brutus

32. Sempronia, mother of Decimus.

33. Marcus Porcius Cato, the Stoic, irreconcilable foe of Caesar.

34. Gnaeus Pompeius, the rival of Caesar. (Pompey).

35. Sextus Pompeius, his son.

YOUNGER CONTEMPORARIES OF ATTICUS—CAESARIANS

36. Publius Clodius, the tribune.

37. Aulus Hirtius, consul in 43 B.C.

38. Gaius Asinius Pollio, lieutenant of Caesar, historian and rhetorician.

39. Gaius Sallustius Crispus, the historian.

40. Gaius Sallustius Crispus, the younger, nephew and heir of No. 39.

41. Marcus Licinius Crassus, of the first triumvirate.

42. Lucius Licinius Lucullus, the conqueror of Mithridates.

43. Marcus Antonius (Mark Antony).

44. Fulvia, his first wife.

45. Cleopatra, Queen of Egypt.

46. Appius Claudius Pulcher, head of the Claudian family, brother of No. 36.

47. Marcus Caelius, young rake, defended by Cicero.

48. Servius Sulpicius Rufus, Stoic and famous lawyer.

49. Gaius Verres, governor of Sicily.

50. Quintus Hortensius Hortalus, the orator, rival of Cicero.

LITERARY FIGURES

51. Publius Vergilius Maro (Vergil).

52. Quintus Horatius Flaccus (Horace).

53. Gaius Valerius Catullus.

54. Marcus Terentius Varro, encyclopedic writer and rhetorician.

55. Quintus Calenus, friend of Varro.

56. Gaius Rubirius, epic poet.

57. Lucius Varius, epic poet.

58. Lucius Ateius, philologist.

59. Santra, philologist.

60. Lucius Valgius, poet.

61. Gaius Cornelius Gallus, poet.

62. Publilius Syrus, writer of mimes.

63. Titus Lucretius Carus, Epicurean poet, author of *De rerum natura,* "On the Nature of Things."

THE MEN OF ATTICUS' BOYHOOD

64. Lucius Cornelius Sulla, the dictator.

65. Gaius Marius, the conqueror of the Cimbri and of Jugurtha.

66. Gaius Marius, the younger, boyhood friend of Atticus.

67. Publius Cornelius Lentulus, called "The Wealthy."

68. Lucius Licinius Crassus, the orator, censor in 92 B.C.

69. Quintus Mucius, Stoic and lawyer.

70. Marcus Antonius, the elder, the orator.

71. Publius Servilius Glaucia   leaders of a revolt in

72. Lucius Appuleius Saturninus   100 B.C.

73. Manius Aemilius Lepidus, a senatorial leader.

74. Lucius Cornelius Cinna, colleague of the elder Marius.

75. Quintus Caecilius, advocate of Verres.

EPICUREANS

76. Lucius Manlius Torquatus

77. Gaius Statilius

78. Titus Catius

79. Timon of Athens, the misanthrope.

80. Philodemus, Greek poet and friend of Atticus.

81. Zeno, founder of the Stoic sect.

II

NON-HISTORICAL PERSONS

82. Saras, an Egyptian emissary of Cleopatra.

83. Lucius Aelius Lamia, fop and spendthrift.

84. Lysanias, emissary of the Nabataean king, Malchus.

85. Aulus Gabinius Serapio, a Romanized Egyptian.

86. Marcus Pomponius ⎱
87. Lucius Caecilius ⎰ cousins of Atticus.

88. Chaerestratus, an Ephesian musician.

89. Theodorus, a Greek philosopher.

90. Sextus Aufidius.

91. Gnaeus Manlius Torquatus.

92. Tyndarus, slave of the elder Caecilius.

93. Dionysius, freedman of Atticus, his chief copyist.

94. Athamas, freedman of Atticus.

95. Salvius ⎱
96. Nicanor ⎰ slaves of Atticus.
97. Alexis

142